Write the Word

on my Heart

A Bible memorization curriculum
for young writers and their families

Katherine Pittman

ANEKO
PRESS

*To my husband, Geoffrey, whose duct-taped Bible and 4-inch stack
of memory cards first inspired my love for the word.*

*And to my dad, whose cartoon drawings of Bible parables helped a young girl
see the Bible wasn't just for parents, but for 6-year-olds, too.*

Skills Practiced:
  Memorization, Recitation, Bible, Sight words, Handwriting, Copywork, Sounding-out simple words

All scripture quotations are from the ESV® Bible, unless otherwise noted.
(The Holy Bible, English Standard Version®),
Copyright © 2001 by Crossway, a publishing ministry of Good News Publishers.
Used by permission. All rights reserved.

Scriptures noted NASB are from the New American Standard Bible® (NASB),
Copyright © 1960, 1962, 1963, 1968, 1971, 1972, 1973, 1975, 1977, 1995
by The Lockman Foundation. Used by permission. www.Lockman.org

Scriptures noted NIV are from The Holy Bible, New International Version® NIV®
Copyright © 1973 1978 1984 2011 by Biblica, Inc. ™
Used by permission. All rights reserved worldwide.

Write the Word

Copyright © 2021 by Katherine Pittman
www.writetheword.com

Cover Photograph: © Noah James Productions LLC
www.noahjamesproductions.com

Aneko Press
www.anekopress.com
Aneko Press, Life Sentence Publishing, and our logos are trademarks of
Life Sentence Publishing, Inc.
203 E. Birch Street
P.O. Box 652
Abbotsford, WI 54405
EDUCATION / Home Schooling
ISBN: 978-1-62245-760-1
10 9 8 7 6 5 4 3 2 1

Printed in Hong Kong.

Why *Write the Word?*

"I have hidden your word in my heart, that I might not sin against you."
Psalm 119:11 NIV

As a young Christian, I was encouraged to memorize the word.

In the beginning, the task seemed tedious and overwhelming. But as my stack of memory cards slowly grew, so did my love for the Lord. He was no longer a faraway God; he became *my* God. When I was uncertain about moving, a memorized verse showed me what to do. When I walked the dark path to my apartment in the dead of night, memorized Psalms stilled my heart. When hard circumstances threatened to overwhelm me, the scriptures, hidden deep in my heart, calmed my soul.

Today, days are busy with homeschooling and toddlers, but the Lord continues to speak through verses memorized long ago. Though I'm not a Bible memory expert, and many have retained much more of the word than I; still, I've tasted the thrill of receiving from him; of dwelling on the implanted word; of standing in awe as he connects verses in my heart. Through seasons of darkness, doubt, and grief, his word has anchored my soul. It's an anchoring I long for my children to experience as well.

And so, the burden for *Write the Word* was born.

Write the Word is a copy work and Bible memory curriculum, originally written to use in my own home. I wanted a consistent way to help my children memorize the word. I wanted them to hear the word and know our Lord had something in there for them. At the same time, I knew the best way for me to continue memorizing was to work *with* my children, bringing the verses to life in our home. So yes, *Write the Word* is written with the heart of a child in view. But *Write the Word* is for you, too. We hope you will memorize these verses alongside your children, sharing them, "when you sit in your house and when you walk along the road and when you lie down and when you rise up." (See Deuteronomy 11:18-21 NASB)

May these verses become not just a memory exercise, but a reference point, directing the hearts of our children to love the Lord and his word, even from their youth.

To God be the Glory,

Katherine

*"You shall therefore impress these words of mine
on your heart and on your soul...
You shall teach them to your sons,
talking of them when you sit in your house
and when you walk along the road
and when you lie down
and when you rise up
You shall write them
on the doorposts of your house
and on your gates
So that your days
and the days of your sons
may be multiplied on the land"*

Deuteronomy 11:18-21 NASB

How does *Write the Word* work?

This book includes 30 verses. Each verse is intended to take one week to learn.

Day 1: Read, repeat, trace, and copy

Read through the verse 2 or 3 times, encouraging your child(ren) to say it with you. After reciting the verse several times together, have your child try on their own. Before they copy and trace the verse, take a moment to discuss what the verse means for them. If you're not sure where to begin, discussion starters and suggested questions are listed at the beginning of each section. Now, through the week, keep your heart open, looking for those teachable moments to apply the verse at home.

Day 2: Find the missing words, read, repeat, trace, and copy

Read the verse together. Today, several words are missing. Can they figure out which ones? Each day, a few more words will be removed, (only short words, so no one gets discouraged with a hard-to-spell one). Once they fill in the missing words (feel free to help), read the verse together. Have your child repeat the verse back to you. Finish by tracing and copying the rest of the verse.

Day 3: Find more missing words; read, repeat, trace, copy, and a puzzle

There are a few more words missing today. Let your child take the lead with the verse today. Can they recite the verse without your help? Say it together a few times and help them spell the missing words if help is needed. (We want to keep this fun, and our focus isn't on spelling.) Trace and copy the verse.
If the verse isn't sticking, you may want to introduce a verse puzzle. You can create your own or find a free download at writetheword.com. Cut out the verse of the week, then cut the words apart and spread them out. Can your child put the verse in order?

Day 4: Even more missing words, trace, copy, and recite together

Before you begin, do they know the verse? They may. Read the verse together, asking them to add the missing words. Now, have your child trace, and copy the whole verse. This is the last day of writing. Hopefully by now, both you and your child have memorized the verse. Pull out the memory puzzle again or try to make up a song about the verse if you are still struggling.

Day 5: Recite the verse for family and friends! Color and display your verse picture; review your memory cards.

It is time to recite! Whether you are in the car, preparing breakfast, or cleaning up the morning dishes—just give your child the verse reference, and let them recite. Then, flip it around. Read the verse to your child and see if they can tell you the reference. (You can let them test you, too.) With every success, give loads of praise. Let them share with Grandma and Grandpa. Let them share with friends or Sunday school teachers. You made it! Awesome!

Color and tear out the go-along verse picture, and **display it** somewhere in your home, where it can be referenced often. **Write out the week's verse** on an index card (or download the free printable cards at writetheword.com). Keep your cards together with a rubber band or on a metal ring. Each Friday, take a few moments to **review the memory cards** from past weeks.

But how do I keep the word *"on my Heart"?*

"You shall therefore impress these words of mine on your heart and on your soul..."
Deuteronomy 11:18-21 NASB

The heart behind *Write the Word* is not only that your children would write out and memorize the word, but also that the word would be **written on their hearts, displayed in their homes, and shared with them day and night.** Parents and guardians, this curriculum is for you, just as much as for your child. Our prayer is that as you memorize these verses with your child, you will begin to use them around the home. We hope you will bring them up with your children in times of correction, in times of fear, and when there is need for encouragement and help. For this reason, we have included these extras to encourage you:

Coloring Sheets for Each Verse

You can use these however you like, but our suggestion is to have your child color the verse sometime during the week they are copying the verse (perhaps on Day 5, when there is no other writing). Then, hang it in your home where it can be referenced often.

Bible Verse Cards

You will need a card for each verse memorized. You can download a free printable set of cards at writetheword.com, or create your own. Keep these cards together, adding the newly completed verse to the stack each week. Choose one day a week (we like Fridays) to review the cards, laying some aside when the stack starts getting thick and you are sure they've been mastered.

Bible Memory Puzzles

On our website, you will also find free downloads for a printable set of go-along verse puzzles. Some children will quickly pick up the verse, but if you find your child struggling (or just want to give them an extra challenge), these puzzles are provided as an additional option to aid with memory work. Cut the words apart and scramble them. Then, let your child try to put the verse in order.

For a child who struggles with handwriting, these words can also be used to fill the blank spaces in the daily exercises. If you're doing this curriculum with a child who struggles with reading, you may try using a song instead or create a verse puzzle using only the first letter of the verse.

Bible Memory Suggestions

Here we share memory tricks, and a few of our favorite ways to get the word into our hearts and homes.

Teaching Tips

We have dedicated a page at the beginning of each section to share why we selected the verses we did, and how you can practically use them in the home. You will also find discussion questions, additional verses, and even a few stories about how these verses have helped our family. We share these with the prayer that the word of God will be written on the hearts of our children, as they are "sitting in [our] house, and when [they] are walking by the way, and when [they] lie down, and when [they] rise...."

Table of Contents

*An asterisk (*) indicates a small portion of the verse was omitted at the beginning or the end.

±Bible scholars often distinguish parts of a verse using a, b, c, etc. While we considered this for other verses, it seemed this may be too confusing for a young child. Only one verse (Isaiah 41:10) is broken up using this method and is memorized over the course of two weeks.

SECTION ONE:
The Beginning

WEEK ONE: Genesis 1:1—*In the beginning, God created the heavens and the earth.*

This first verse in the Bible seemed like a good place to start. It is short, easy to memorize, and the foundation of our faith. In the beginning...God. Before everything...God. As you memorize this week, try to point out aspects of God's creation. The stars at night. The sun that warms the earth. The little budding flower and the buried seed are all reminders from the Lord of creation, pointing us to himself. Whether you are a seasoned Christian or a young child, it is assuring to remember: the same God who created the heavens and the earth, also created and cares for *you*.

Thoughts for Further Discussion and Study:

- "The heavens declare the glory of God" the Psalmist writes (Psalm 19:1) and "his eternal power and divine nature, have been clearly perceived...in the things that have been made" Paul tells us (Romans 1:20). Children are often fascinated with flowers, bugs, seeds, and dirt. Take a moment to ponder how God speaks, even through these small details of creation. Have you ever taken a moment to ponder the life cycle of a seed? How it falls into the earth and dies, bringing forth much fruit? Does this not remind us of another seed, our Lord Jesus, who fell into the earth and died, to bring forth much fruit? Have we ever stopped to ponder that the glorious gospel is written into every aspect of creation? The Creator knew, from the foundation of the world, that he would come and die. And he wrote his story into every flower and tree, into animals and plants. The more our hearts ponder the creation, the more wonderful our Creator becomes. So, pause this week. Explore the outdoors. God tells us there is glory in his creation, so go out and observe. Where do you see him? Even if your child doesn't catch the gospel connection, let them just be in awe of his creation, reminding them in the still moments that it was all created by him.

Genesis 1:1

in the beginning, God created the heavens and the earth

Day 1: New week, new verse! Read the verse together 3x, then trace it, and copy below.

Day 2: Can you figure out which words are missing? Read the verse together 3x, then trace it and copy below.

In the beginning, _____ created the heavens and the earth.

Genesis 1:1

Day 3: More missing words! Can you recite the verse without help? Say the verse together 3x; then trace and copy below.

In _____ beginning, _____

created _____ heavens

and _____ earth.

Genesis 1:1

Day 4: Can you say the verse without help today? Fill in all the missing words, trace, and copy the verse below.

_____ _____ beginning, _____

created _____ heavens

_____ _____ earth.

Genesis 1:1

In the beginning, God created the heavens and the earth. In the beginning, God created the heavens and the earth. In the beginning, God created the heavens and the earth. In the beginning, God created the heavens and the earth. In the beginning, God created the heavens and the earth. In the beginning, God created the heavens and the earth. In the beginning, God created the heavens and the earth. In the beginning, God created the heavens and the earth. In the beginning, God created the heavens and the earth. In the beginning, God created the heavens and the earth. In the beginning, God created the heavens and the earth. In the beginning, God created

Day 5

No Copy Work!

Recite Genesis 1:1 for family & friends

Color or highlight the verse picture, then tear it out and display it somewhere you'll see it often

Write out Genesis 1:1 on a memory card
(or use the free printable cards at writetheword.com)
and begin your memory stack

Congratulations!

You've begun a wonderful habit

God created the heavens and the earth. In the beginning, God created the heavens and the earth. In the beginning, God created the heavens and the earth. In the beginning, God created the heavens and the earth. In the beginning, God created the heavens and the earth. In the beginning, God created the heavens and the earth. In the beginning, God created the heavens and the earth. In the beginning, God created the heavens and the earth. In the beginning, God created the heavens and the earth. In the beginning, God created the heavens and the earth. In the beginning, God created the heavens and the

In the beginning GOD CREATED the heavens and the earth

Genesis 1:1

SECTION TWO:

A call to "Come"

WEEK TWO: Matthew 19:14—*But Jesus said, "Let the little children come to me and do not hinder them."*

As we begin this year through the scriptures, we want our children to know God's heart for them. Jesus says, "come," sit on my lap as I share with the crowds (Matthew 19:14). Another time he says, "whoever receives [a] child... receives me" (Mark 9:37). In every interaction Jesus has with children, his welcoming call assures them: you are not a bother, you are not a pest, you are not in the way (as some around you may think). His call, his extended hand, the way he stops and receives the interruptions, the way he brings the children alongside, all show our Lord's heart and care for even the youngest ones.

Thoughts for Further Discussion and Study:

- God is calling you to come and get to know him this year through his word. He never wants you to stand far off. He never says, "this is just for adults." When our Lord sees the little children, he extends his hands and says, "Let the little children come."
- God is for you. Even if someone wants to dismiss you, or treat you harshly, or say you don't matter, God is always for you. (And parents, when our actions fail to express this to our children, it is good to go back and say so: "I'm sorry, I wasn't expressing God's heart when I did that.")

Matthew 19:14*

But Jesus said, "Let the little children come to me and do not hinder them"

Day 1: New week, new verse! Read the verse together 3x, then trace it, and copy below.

But Jesus said, "Let the little children come to me and do not hinder them."

Matthew 19:14

Day 2: Can you figure out which words are missing? Read the verse together 3x, then trace it and copy below.

But Jesus said, "_____ the little children come _____ _____ and do _____ hinder them."

Matthew 19:14

Day 3: More missing words! Can you recite the verse without help? Say the verse together 3x; then trace and copy below.

Day 4: Can you say the verse without help today? Fill in all the missing words, trace, and copy the verse below.

_____ Jesus said, "_____

_____ little children come

hinder _____."

Matthew 19:14

_____

_____

_____

_____

_____

but Jesus said, Let the little children come to me and do not hinder them, for to such belongs the kingdom of heaven. but Jesus said, Let the little children come to me and do not hinder them, for. to such belongs the kingdom of heaven. but Jesus said, Let the little children come to me and do not hinder them, for to such belongs the kingdom of heaven. but Jesus said, Let the little children come to me and do not hinder them, for to such belongs the kingdom of heaven. but Jesus said, Let the little children come to me and do not hinder them, for to such belongs the kingdom of heaven. but Jesus said, Let the little children come to me and do not hinder them, for to such belongs the kingdom

Day 5

No Copy Work!

Recite Matthew 19:14* for family & friends

Color or highlight the verse picture, then tear it out
and display it somewhere you'll see it often

Write out Matthew 19:14 on a memory card
(or use the free printable cards at writetheword.com)
and add it to your memory stack

Review the cards in your memory pile

of heaven. but Jesus said, Let the little children come to me and do not hinder them, for to such belongs the kingdom of heaven. but Jesus said, Let the little children come to me and do not hinder them, for to such belongs the kingdom of heaven. but Jesus said, Let the little children come to me and do not hinder them, for to such belongs the kingdom of heaven. but Jesus said, Let the little children come to me and do not hinder them, for to such belongs the kingdom of heaven. but Jesus said, Let the little children come to me and do not hinder them, for to such belongs the kingdom of heaven. but Jesus said, Let the little children come to me and do not hinder them, for to such belongs the kingdom

but Jesus said:

Let the *little*

CHILDREN

come

to me

and do not **hinder**

them

Matthew 19:14

SECTION THREE:

A call to "Seek"

WEEK THREE: Jeremiah 29:13—*You will seek me and find me when you seek me with all your heart.*

WEEK FOUR: Matthew 6:33—*But seek first the kingdom of God and his righteousness, and all these things will be added to you.*

This first year through *Write the Word* is meant to be a time of seeking. Together, we are seeking God's heart. If God wants our children to come to him, what does he want to say? Does he have any specific words for the problems that they will run into as a 6- or 7- or 8-year-old? What does he say about being afraid? Feeling hopeless? What about disobedience, honoring parents, or the way we speak and live? As our children grow, we want to help them develop the habit of seeking the Lord in everything.

Thoughts for Further Discussion and Study:

- We may think or feel one way, but we need to seek God to discover his heart.
- Seeking is never half-hearted. What words does God connect with his command to "seek"? (*first, all your heart*)
- Why does God want us to seek him? Why does he sometimes "hide"?
- Do you like to play hide-and-seek? Do you like being the hider or the seeker? Why? What is your reaction when you are found? (*There is joy in finding, and also joy in being found.*)

Jeremiah 29:13

You will seek me and find me when you seek me with all your heart

Day 1: New week, new verse! Read the verse together 3x, then trace it, and copy below.

You will seek me and find me when you seek me with all your heart. Jeremiah 29:13

Day 2: Can you figure out which words are missing? Read the verse together 3x, then trace it and copy below.

You will seek ___ and find ___ when you seek ___ with all your heart. Jeremiah 29:13

Day 3: More missing words! Can you recite the verse without help? Say the verse together 3x; then trace and copy below.

You ____ ____ seek ____ and find ____ when ____ seek ____ with ____ your heart. Jeremiah 29:13

Day 4: Can you say the verse without help today? Fill in all the missing words, trace, and copy the verse below.

You ____ ____ ____ ____ ____ ____ ____

find ____ when ____ ____ ____

____ with ____ ____ your heart.

Jeremiah 29:13

You will seek me and find me when you seek me with all your heart. You will seek me and find me when you seek me with all your heart. You will seek me and find me when you seek me with all your heart. You will seek me and find me when you seek me with all your heart. You will seek me and find me when you seek me with all your heart. You will seek me and find me when you seek me with all your heart. You will seek me and find me when you seek me with all your heart. You will seek me and find me when you seek me with all your heart. You will seek me and find me when you seek me with all your heart.

Day 5

No Copy Work!

Recite Jeremiah 29:13 for family & friends

Color or highlight the verse picture, then tear it out and display it somewhere you'll see it often

Write out Jeremiah 29:13 on a memory card
(or use the free printable cards at writetheword.com)
and add it to your memory stack

Review the cards in your memory pile

heart. You will seek me and find me when you seek me with all your heart. You will seek me and find me when you seek me with all your heart. You will seek me and find me when you seek me with all your heart. You will seek me and find me when you seek me with all your heart. You will seek me and find me when you seek me with all your heart. You will seek me and find me when you seek me with all your heart. You will seek me and find me when you seek me with all your heart. You will seek me and find me when you seek me with all your heart. You will seek me and find me when you seek me with all your heart. You will seek me and find me when you seek me with all your heart. You will seek me and find me when you seek me with all your heart. You will

You will [W I L L] seek me

and me

find me

when [W H E N]

you seek me

with all your

heart

Jeremiah 29:13

Matthew 6:33

But seek first the kingdom of God and his righteousness, and all these things will be added to you

Day 1: New week, new verse! Read the verse together 3x, then trace it, and copy below.

But seek first the kingdom of God and his righteousness, and all these things will be added to you. Matthew 6:33

Day 2: Can you figure out which words are missing? Read the verse together 3x, then trace it and copy below.

But _____ _____ first the kingdom of _____ and his righteousness, and all these things will be added to _____ . Matthew 6:33

Day 3: More missing words! Can you recite the verse without help? Say the verse together 3x; then trace and copy below.

But _____ first _____

kingdom ___ ___ and _____

righteousness, and all

these things _____

added to _____.

Matthew 6:33

Day 4: Can you say the verse without help today? Fill in all the missing words, trace, and copy the verse below.

first

kingdom

righteousness,

these things

added

Matthew 6:33

But seek first the kingdom of God and his righteousness, and all these things will be added to you. But seek first the kingdom of God and his righteousness, and all these things will be added to you. But seek first the kingdom of God and his righteousness, and all these things will be added to you. But seek first the kingdom of God and his righteousness, and all these things will be added to you. But seek first the kingdom of God and his righteousness, and all these

Day 5

No Copy Work!

Recite Matthew 6:33 for family & friends

Color or highlight the verse picture, then tear it out
and display it somewhere you'll see it often

Write out Matthew 6:33 on a memory card
(or use the free printable cards at writetheword.com)
and add it to your memory stack

Review the cards in your memory pile

kingdom of God and his righteousness, and all these things will be added to you. But seek first the kingdom of God and his righteousness, and all these things will be added to you. But seek first the kingdom of God and his righteousness, and all these things will be added to you. But seek first the kingdom of God and his righteousness, and all these things will be added to you. But seek first the kingdom of God and his righteousness, and all these things will be added to you. But seek first the kingdom of God and his righteousness, and all these things will be added to you. But seek first the kingdom of God and his righteousness, and all these things will be added to you. But seek first the kingdom of God and his righteousness, and all these things will be added to you. But seek first the kingdom of God and his righteousness, and all these things will be added to

But seek 1st the kingdom of God and his righteousness and all these things will be added to you

Matthew 6:33

SECTION FOUR:

In times of Fear

WEEK FIVE: Psalm 56:3—*When I am afraid, I put my trust in you.*

WEEK SIX: Isaiah 41:10a—*Fear not, for I am with you; be not dismayed, for I am your God;*

WEEK SEVEN: Isaiah 41:10b—*I will strengthen you, I will help you, I will uphold you with my righteous right hand.*

WEEK EIGHT: Romans 10:13—*For everyone who calls on the name of the Lord will be saved.*

Fear is one of the most common and easiest ways to first introduce the Lord to our children. Are they afraid at night? Before a doctor's visit? After a bad dream? This world is filled with fearful, scary things. But instead of telling our children, "monsters don't exist" or "go back to bed," acknowledge their fears, using each troubled moment to point them back to the God who meets us in our fears. The simple promise, "I am with you," or "I will help you," is not just a soothing comfort for small children, but a word to remember for life.

It should also be noted that while we often think of Romans 10:13 as "saved" from hell, the word "saved" can also refer to being saved from a difficult situation (Paul speaks of being saved from the lion's mouth (see 2 Timothy 4:17).) We have always encouraged our children that there is power in the name of Jesus. If they ever have a scary dream, or get into a dark situation—even if they don't know what to say—"call on the name of Jesus," we've encouraged them, and he will send help. I cannot stress enough the blessing of knowing and applying this simple verse. In the littlest years, teach them to come to him, to seek him, and to call on the name of Jesus in times of trouble.

Thoughts for Further Discussion and Study:

- Can they remember a time when they were afraid? What made them afraid? What brought them peace?
- Encourage your children to call upon the name of Jesus when they are afraid. Remind them that even when you are not around, the Lord hears their call for help.

Psalm 56:3

When I am afraid, I put my trust in you

Day 1: New week, new verse! Read the verse together 3x, then trace it, and copy below.

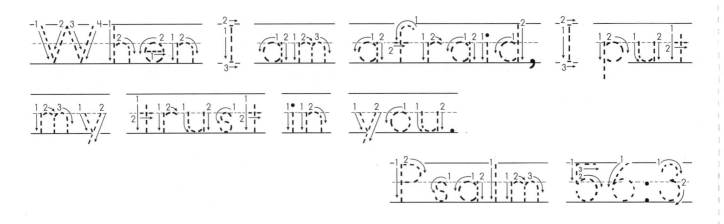

When I am afraid, I put my trust in you. Psalm 56:3

Day 2: Can you figure out which words are missing? Read the verse together 3x, then trace it and copy below.

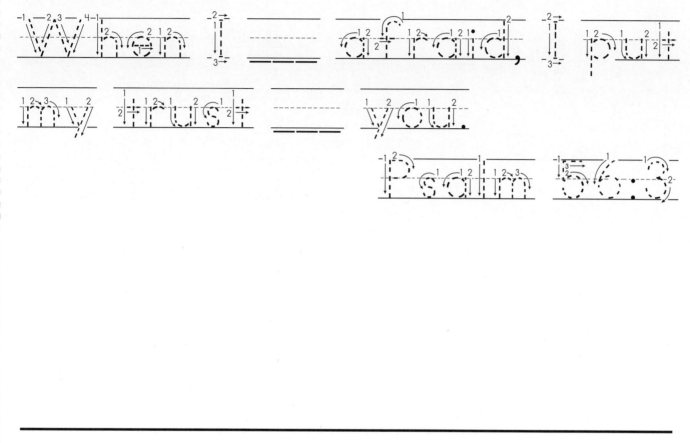

When I ___ afraid, I put my trust ___ you. Psalm 56:3

Day 3: More missing words! Can you recite the verse without help? Say the verse together 3x; then trace and copy below.

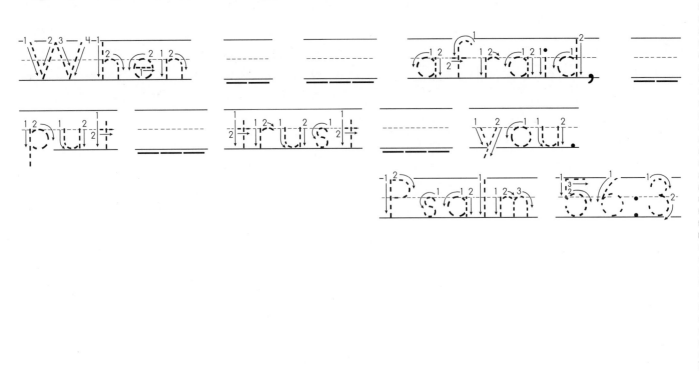

When ___ ___ ___ afraid, ___
put ___ trust ___ you.
Psalm 56:3

Day 4: Can you say the verse without help today? Fill in all the missing words, trace, and copy the verse below.

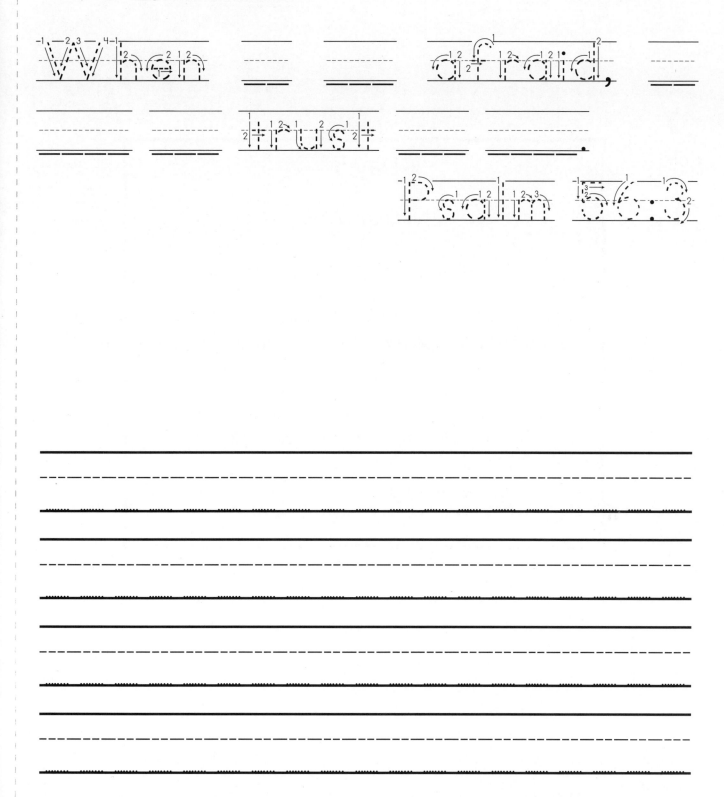

I put my trust in you. When I am afraid, I put my trust in you. When I am afraid, I put my trust in you. When I am afraid, I put my trust in you. When I am afraid, I put my trust in you. When I am afraid, I put my trust in you. When I am afraid, I put my trust in you. When I am afraid, I put my trust in you. When I am afraid, I put my trust in you. When I am afraid, I put my trust in you. When I am afraid, I put my trust in you. When I am afraid, I put my trust in you.

Day 5

No Copy Work!

Recite Psalm 56:3 for family & friends

Color or highlight the verse picture, then tear it out
and display it somewhere you'll see it often

Write out Psalm 56:3 on a memory card
(or use the free printable cards at writetheword.com)
and add it to your memory stack

Review the cards in your memory pile

When I am afraid, I put my trust in you. When I am afraid, I put my trust in you. When I am afraid, I put my trust in you. When I am afraid, I put my trust in you. When I am afraid, I put my trust in you. When I am afraid, I put my trust in you. When I am afraid, I put my trust in you. When I am afraid, I put my trust in you. When I am afraid, I put my trust in you. When I am afraid, I put my trust in you. When I am afraid, I put my trust in you. When I am afraid, I put my trust in you. When I am afraid, I put my trust in you. When I am afraid, I put my trust in you. When I am afraid, I put my trust in you. When I am afraid, I put my trust in you. When I am afraid, I put my trust in you. When I am afraid, I put my trust in you.

When *I am* afraid *I put my* TRUST in **You**

Psalm 56:3

Isaiah 41:10a

Fear not, for I am with you;
be not dismayed,
for I am your God

Day 1: New week, new verse! Read the verse together 3x, then trace it, and copy below.

Fear not, for I am with your, be not dismayed, for I am your God.
Isaiah 41:10a

Day 2: Can you figure out which words are missing? Read the verse together 3x, then trace it and copy below.

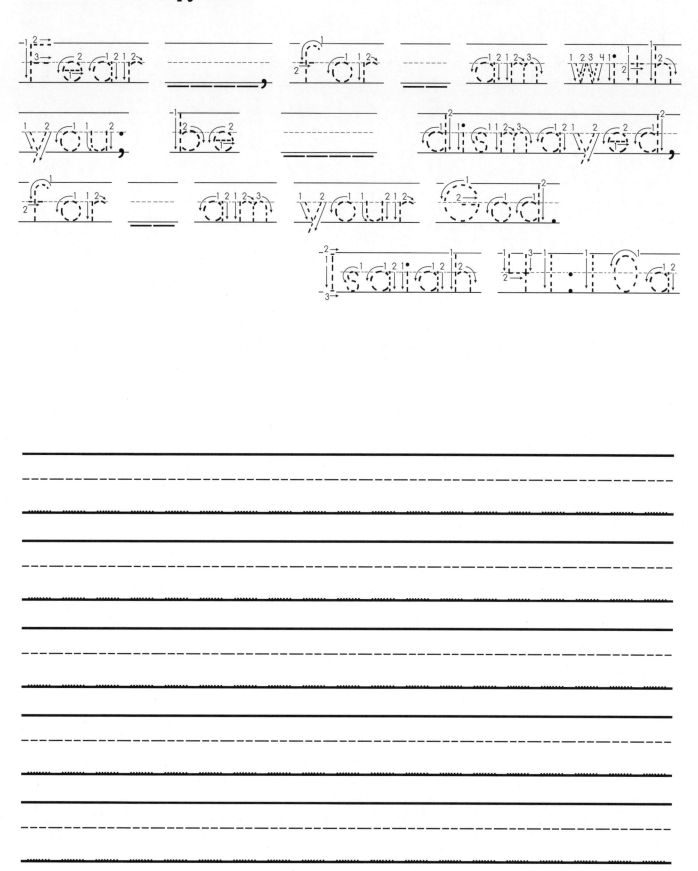

Fear _____, for _ am with you; be _ _ dismayed, for _ am your God. Isaiah 41:10a

Day 3: More missing words! Can you recite the verse without help? Say the verse together 3x; then trace and copy below.

Fear _____, for ___ ___ with you; be ___ dismayed, for ___ ___ your _____.

Isaiah 41:10a

Day 4: Can you say the verse without help today? Fill in all the missing words, trace, and copy the verse below.

Fear _____ , _____ _____ _____ with _____ ; be _____ dismayed, _____ _____ _____ your _____ .

Isaiah 41:10a

Fear not, for I am with you; be not dismayed for I am your God; I will strengthen you, I will help you, I will uphold you with my righteous right hand. Fear not, for I am with you; be not dismayed for I am your God; I will strengthen you, I will help you, I will uphold you with my righteous right hand. Fear not, for I am with you; be not dismayed for I am your God; I will strengthen you, I will help you, I will uphold you with my righteous right hand.

Day 5

No Copy Work!

Recite Isaiah 41:10a for family & friends

Color or highlight the verse picture, then tear it out
and display it somewhere you'll see it often

Write out Isaiah 41:10a on a memory card
(or use the free printable cards at writetheword.com)
and add it to your memory stack

Review the cards in your memory pile

strengthen you, I will help you, I will uphold you with my righteous right hand. Fear not, for I am with you; be not dismayed for I am your God; I will strengthen you, I will help you, I will uphold you with my righteous right hand. Fear not, for I am with you; be not dismayed for I am your God; I will strengthen you, I will help you, I will uphold you with my righteous right hand. Fear not, for I am with you; be not dismayed for I am your God; I will strengthen you, I will help you, I will uphold you with my righteous right hand. Fear not, for I am with you; be not dismayed for I am your God; I will strengthen you, I will help you, I will uphold you with my righteous right hand. Fear not, for I am with you; be not dismayed for I am your God; I will strengthen you, I will help you, I will uphold you with my righteous right hand. Fear not, for I am with you; be not dismayed for I am your God; I will

FEAR NOT
for **I am**
with you
BE NOT DISMAYED
for *I am*
your
God

Isaiah 41:10a

Isaiah 41:10b

*I will strengthen you,
I will help you,
I will uphold you
with my righteous right hand*

Day 1: New week, new verse! Read the verse together 3x, then trace it, and copy below.

I will strengthen you, I will help you, I will uphold you with my righteous right hand. Isaiah 41:10b

Day 2: Can you figure out which words are missing? Read the verse together 3x, then trace it and copy below.

_____ will strengthen _____, _____ will help _____, _____ will uphold _____ with my righteous right hand. Isaiah 41:10b

Day 3: More missing words! Can you recite the verse without help? Say the verse together 3x; then trace and copy below.

strengthen _____,

help _____, ___ _____

uphold _____ with my

righteous right hand.

Isaiah 41:10b

Day 4: Can you say the verse without help today? Fill in all the missing words, trace, and copy the verse below.

_____ ___ ____ strengthen ____,

___ ____ __ help _____, __ ____

uphold ____ ____ ____

righteous right ___ .

Isaiah 41:10b

_____
- -
_____
- -
_____
- -
_____
- -
_____
- -
_____

Fear not, for I am with you; be not dismayed for I am your God; I will strengthen you, I will help you, I will uphold you with my righteous right hand. Fear not, for I am with you; be not dismayed for I am your God; I will strengthen you, I will help you, I will uphold you with my righteous right hand. Fear not, for I am with you; be not dismayed for I am your God; I will strengthen you, I will help you, I will uphold you with my righteous right hand. Fear not, for I am with you; be not dismayed for I am your God; I will strengthen you, I will help you, I will uphold you with my righteous right hand. Fear not, for I am with you; be not dismayed for I am your God; I will

Day 5

No Copy Work!

Recite Isaiah 41:10 (a & b) for family & friends

Color or highlight the verse picture, then tear it out and display it somewhere you'll see it often

Add part b to your Isaiah card, or create a new one (or use the free printable cards at writetheword.com) and add it to your memory stack

Review the cards in your memory pile

strengthen you, I will help you, I will uphold you with my righteous right hand. Fear not, for I am with you; be not dismayed for I am your God; I will strengthen you, I will help you, I will uphold you with my righteous right hand. Fear not, for I am with you; be not dismayed for I am your God; I will strengthen you, I will help you, I will uphold you with my righteous right hand. Fear not, for I am with you; be not dismayed for I am your God; I will strengthen you, I will help you, I will uphold you with my righteous right hand. Fear not, for I am with you; be not dismayed for I am your God; I will strengthen you, I will help you, I will uphold you with my righteous right hand. Fear not, for I am with you; be not dismayed for I am your God; I will

I will
strengthen you
I will
help you
I will
uphold you
with my
righteous

Draw a picture of yourself being held by God's "righteous right hand"

R I G H T   H A N D

Isaiah 41:10b

Romans 10:13

For everyone who calls on the name of the Lord will be saved

Day 1: New week, new verse! Read the verse together 3x, then trace it, and copy below.

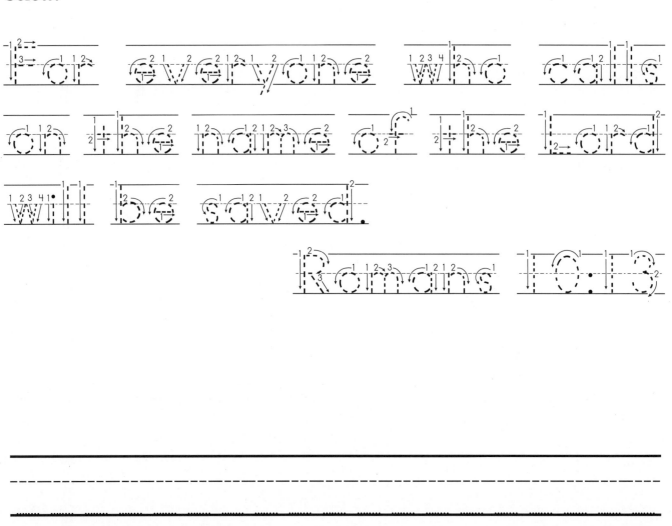

For everyone who calls on the name of the Lord will be saved.

Romans 10:13

Day 2: Can you figure out which words are missing? Read the verse together 3x, then trace it and copy below.

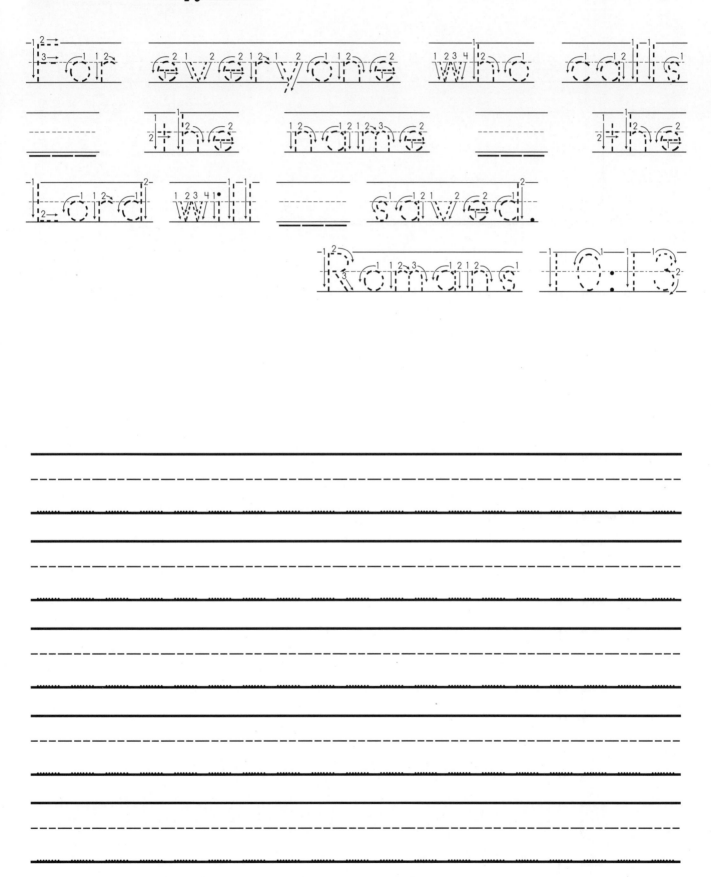

For everyone who calls __ the name __ the Lord will __ saved. Romans 10:13

Day 3: More missing words! Can you recite the verse without help? Say the verse together 3x; then trace and copy below.

_____ everyone who calls

__ __ name __ __

Lord _____ __ saved.

Romans 10:13

Day 4: Can you say the verse without help today? Fill in all the missing words, trace, and copy the verse below.

_ _ _   everyone _ _   _ _
_ _ _   _ _   _ _

_ _   _ _   name _   _   _ _   _ _

Lord _ _   _ _   _ _   saved.

Romans 10:13

_____
- -
....
_____
- -
....
_____
- -
....
_____
- -
....
_____
- -
....

Day 5

No Copy Work!

Recite Romans 10:13 for family & friends

Color or highlight the verse picture, then tear it out and display it somewhere you'll see it often

Write out Romans 10:13 on a memory card
(or use the free printable cards at writetheword.com)
and add it to your memory stack

Review the cards in your memory pile

FOR

everyone WHO CALLS ON

the name

OF THE LORD

will be

saved

Romans 10:13

SECTION FIVE:

Obedience

WEEK NINE: Proverbs 1:8—*Hear, my son, your father's instruction, and forsake not your mother's teaching.*

WEEK TEN: Colossians 3:20—*Children, obey your parents in everything, for this pleases the Lord.*

If you grew up in the church, you likely learned, "Children, obey your parents in the Lord, for this is right," from Ephesians 6. I chose the shorter version in Colossians, but there is a reason the Lord repeatedly gives this instruction to children. The call to obedience is probably *the first and most common way the Lord begins to expose a child's wandering, sinful heart*. They may not want to obey and submit to your household rules (neither did Lucifer, neither did Adam and Eve). But there is a reason the Lord lumps disobedience to parents in with other sins such as slander, hatred of God, and even murder (see 2 Timothy 3:2, Romans 1:30). As Christian parents, we want to help our children see first, Christ is the head, both of his body and of the family; and second, we are called to submit to him. We don't want to be like Lucifer who lifted up his head against God. We want to obey from the heart, willingly. The call to obey also exposes our failure. It shows a young child that he too, is like Adam and can so easily go this rebellious way of Satan. As our children begin to understand their sinful nature, they also begin to see their true need for Christ.

Thoughts for Further Discussion and Study:

- When it comes to obedience, God gives us a choice (The Garden of Eden) but he also often *tells us* what to choose (see Deuteronomy 30). What will their choice be?
- It's hard to obey! How can we make it easier in that moment to choose what's right?
- Can they think of a time when they obeyed? How did it make them feel? What about a time they disobeyed? How did that make them feel?
- Why is our obedience such a big deal to God? (If they're not familiar with Lucifer's fall from heaven, you can gently introduce this story (see Isaiah 14, Ezekiel 28), reminding that our Lord Jesus willingly submitted to the Father's plan and order (see Philippians 2), but Satan resisted, rebelled, and tried to be in charge.
- Obedience isn't purposeless. In God's original command (the 5th commandment), God included phrases like, "that it may go well with you" and "that you may have a long life on the earth" (see Exodus 20:12, Deuteronomy 5:16, Ephesians 6:3). Can they think of an example where obedience would make something "go well with you"?

Proverbs 1:8

Hear, my son, your father's instruction, and forsake not your mother's teaching

Day 1: New week, new verse! Read the verse together 3x, then trace it, and copy below.

Hear, my son, your
father's instruction, and
forsake not your
mother's teaching.
Proverbs 1:8

Day 2: Can you figure out which words are missing? Read the verse together 3x, then trace it and copy below.

Hear, _____ son, your father's instruction, _____ forsake _____ your mother's teaching.

Proverbs 1:8

Day 3: More missing words! Can you recite the verse without help? Say the verse together 3x; then trace and copy below.

Hear, _____ _____, your father's instruction, _____ forsake _____ your mother's teaching. Proverbs 1:8

Day 4: Can you say the verse without help today? Fill in all the missing words, trace, and copy the verse below.

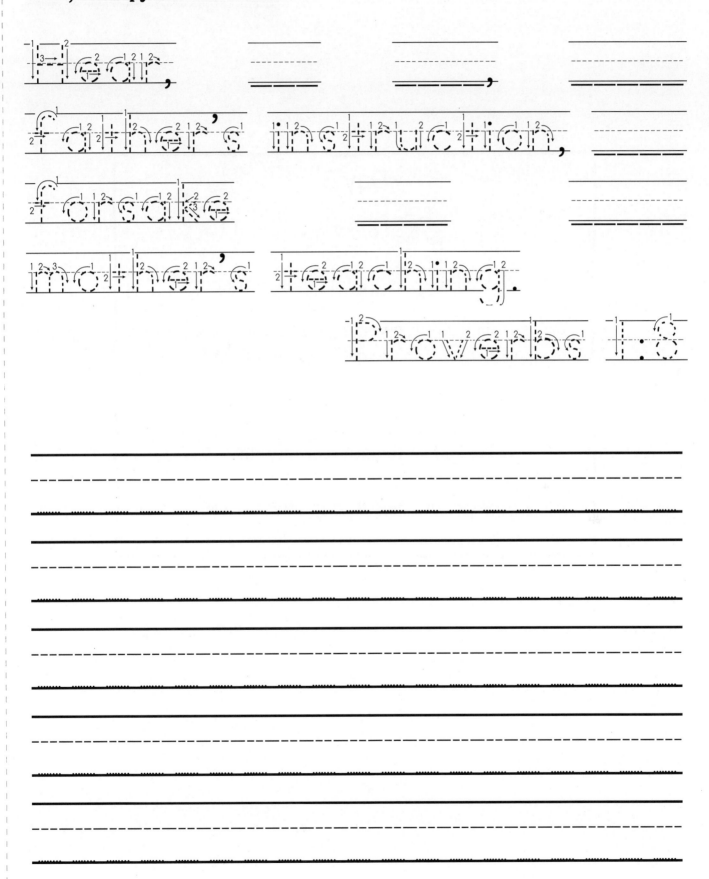

Hear, _____ _____,
father's instruction, _____
forsake _____
mother's teaching.
Proverbs 1:8

Hear, my son, your father's instruction and forsake not your mother's teaching. Hear, my son, your father's instruction and forsake not your mother's teaching. Hear, my son, your father's instruction and forsake not your mother's teaching. Hear, my son, your father's instruction and forsake not your mother's teaching. Hear, my son, your father's instruction and forsake not your mother's teaching. Hear, my son, your father's instruction and forsake not your mother's teaching. Hear, my son, your father's instruction and forsake not your mother's teaching. Hear, my son, your

Day 5

No Copy Work!

Recite Proverbs 1:8 for family & friends

Color or highlight the verse picture, then tear it out
and display it somewhere you'll see it often

Write out Proverbs 1:8 on a memory card
(or use the free printable cards at writetheword.com)
and add it to your memory stack

Review the cards in your memory pile

my son, your father's instruction and forsake not your mother's teaching. Hear, my son, your father's instruction and forsake not your mother's teaching. Hear, my son, your father's instruction and forsake not your mother's teaching. Hear, my son, your father's instruction and forsake not your mother's teaching. Hear, my son, your father's instruction and forsake not your mother's teaching. Hear, my son, your father's instruction and forsake not your mother's teaching. Hear, my son, your father's instruction and forsake not your mother's teaching. Hear, my son, your father's instruction and forsake not your mother's teaching. Hear, my son, your father's instruction and forsake not your mother's teaching. Hear, my son, your father's instruction and forsake not your mother's teaching. Hear, my son, your father's instruction and forsake not your mother's teaching. Hear, my son, your father's instruction and forsake not your mother's teaching. Hear, my son, your father's instruction and forsake not your mother's teaching.

Hear, my son
your
Father's
instruction
and forsake not
your Mother's
teaching

Yes, Mommy

Right away, Dad!

Proverbs 1:8

Colossians 3:20

Children, obey your parents in everything, for this pleases the Lord

Day 1: New week, new verse! Read the verse together 3x, then trace it, and copy below.

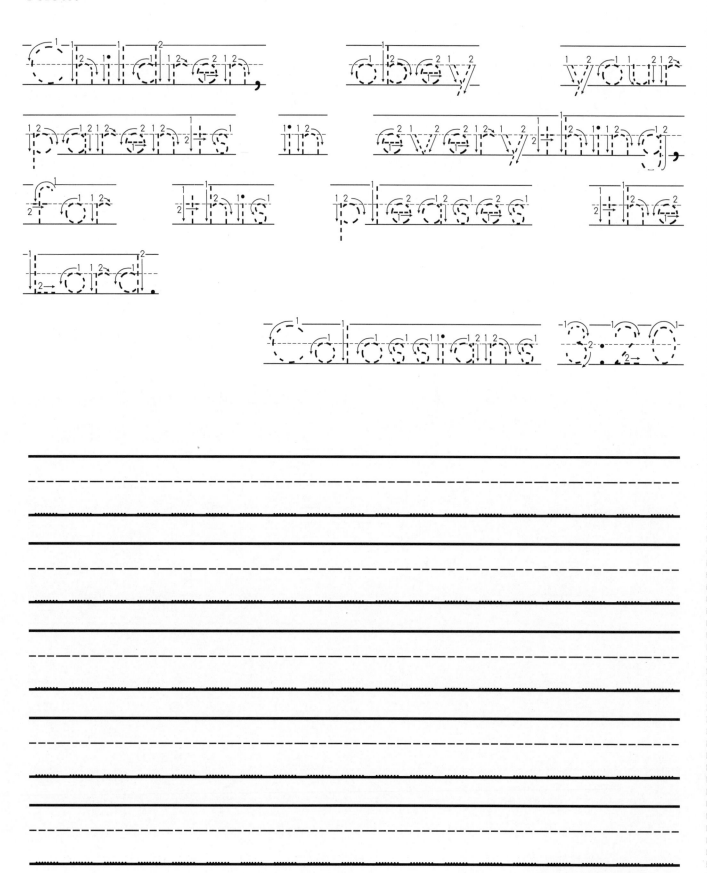

Children, obey your parents in everything, for this pleases the Lord.

Colossians 3:20

Day 2: Can you figure out which words are missing? Read the verse together 3x, then trace it and copy below.

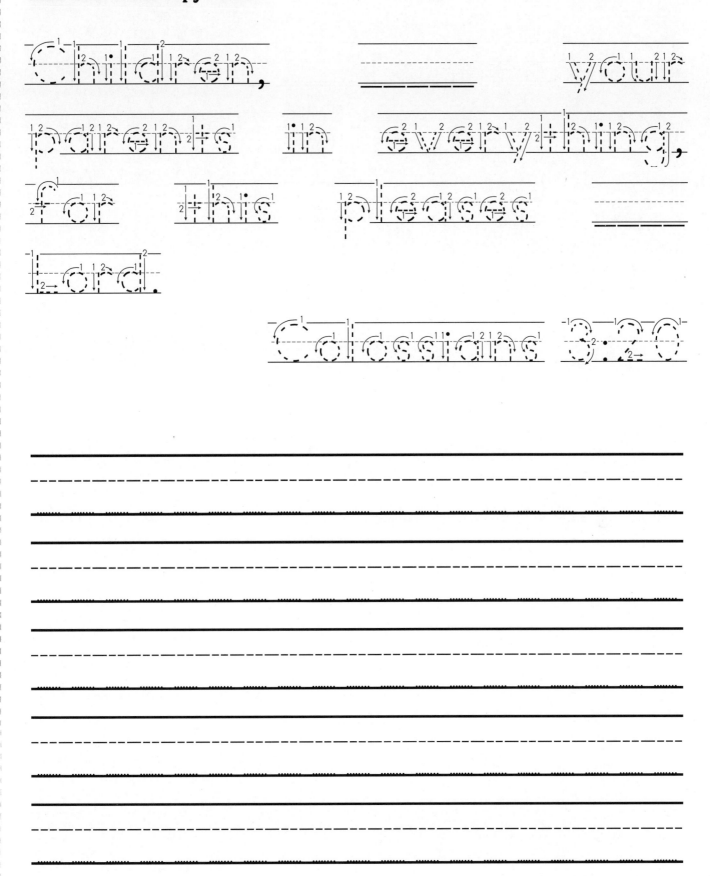

Children, _____ your parents in everything, for this pleases _____ Lord.

Colossians 3:20

Day 3: More missing words! Can you recite the verse without help? Say the verse together 3x; then trace and copy below.

Children, _____ _____ your parents _____ everything, for _____ pleases _____ Lord.

Colossians 3:20

Day 4: Can you say the verse without help today? Fill in all the missing words, trace, and copy the verse below.

Children, _____ _____

parents _____ everything,

pleases _____

_____.

Colossians 3:20

for this pleases the Lord. Children obey your parents in everything, for this pleases the Lord. Children obey your parents in everything, for this pleases the Lord. Children obey your parents in everything, for this pleases the Lord. Children obey your parents in everything, for this pleases the Lord. Children obey your parents in everything, for this pleases the Lord. Children obey your parents in everything, for this pleases the Lord. Children obey your parents in everything, for this pleases the Lord. Children obey your parents in everything, for this pleases the Lord. Children obey your parents in

Day 5

No Copy Work!

Recite Colossians 3:20 for family & friends

Color or highlight the verse picture, then tear it out
and display it somewhere you'll see it often

Write out Colossians 3:20 on a memory card
(or use the free printable cards at writetheword.com)
and add it to your memory stack

Review the cards in your memory pile

your parents in everything, for this pleases the Lord. Children obey your parents in everything, for this pleases the Lord. Children obey your parents in everything, for this pleases the Lord. Children obey your parents in everything, for this pleases the Lord. Children obey your parents in everything, for this pleases the Lord. Children obey your parents for this pleases the Lord. Children obey your parents in everything, for this pleases the Lord. Children obey your parents in everything, for this pleases the Lord. Children obey your parents in everything, for this pleases the Lord. Children obey your parents in everything, for this pleases the Lord. Children obey your parents in everything, for this pleases the Lord. Children obey your parents in everything, for this pleases the Lord. Children obey your parents in everything, for this pleases the Lord. Children obey your parents for this

CHILDREN

obey

your

parents

in everything

for

this pleases

the

Lord

Colossians 3:20

SECTION SIX:

WEEK ELEVEN: Proverbs 15:1—*A soft answer turns away wrath, but a harsh word stirs up anger.*

WEEK TWELVE: Psalm 34:13—*Keep your tongue from evil and your lips from speaking deceit.*

WEEK THIRTEEN: 1 Thessalonians 5:11—*Therefore encourage one another and build one another up, just as you are doing.*

WEEK FOURTEEN: Psalm 19:14—*Let the words of my mouth and the meditation of my heart, be acceptable in your sight, O Lord.*

In our home, these verses are repeated almost daily, and phrases like, "Does that build up?" or "Remember your soft answer" are used often. Whether you have a houseful of kids, or an only child, all of us must deal with conflict at some point. These verses are quick reminders to let our words be "full of grace, seasoned with salt" (Colossians 4:6 NIV), and serve as a great encouragement to use our tongues for building up, and not tearing down.

Thoughts for Further Discussion and Study:

- What does it mean to have a "soft answer"? ("I'm sorry," "I didn't mean to," or "Is there anything I can do?" are all "soft answer" responses that help to melt an angry heart.)
- What are some ways to "encourage and build up"?
- Do they think their words are "acceptable in his sight"?
- In the middle of a conflict try asking: "Is that a soft answer?" or "How can we turn that into a soft answer?" or "What could we say right now to encourage or build _____ up?"

Proverbs 15:1

A soft answer turns away wrath, but a harsh word stirs up anger

Day 1: New week, new verse! Read the verse together 3x, then trace it, and copy below.

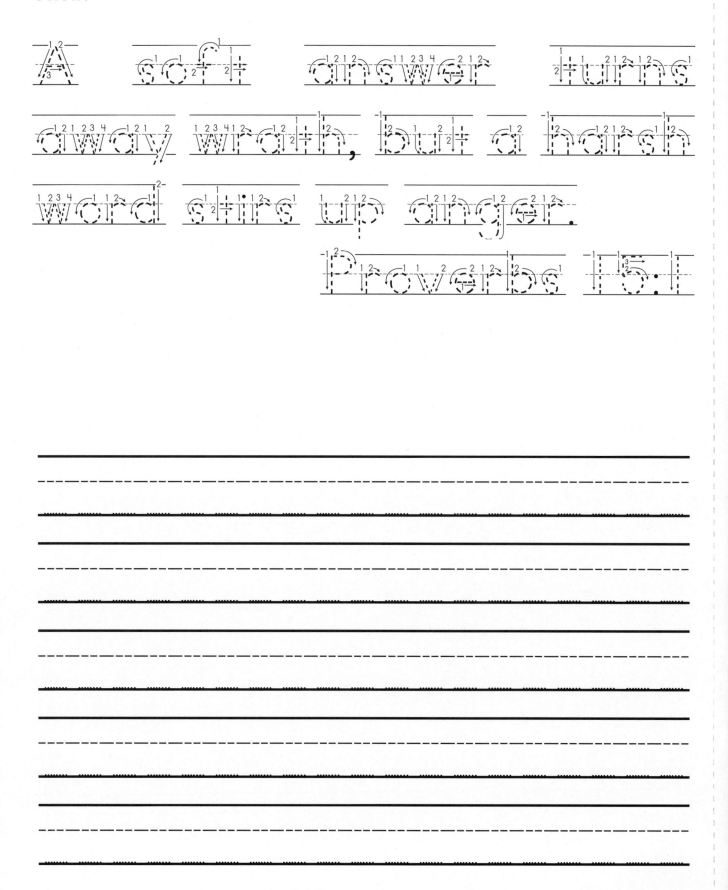

A soft answer turns away wrath, but a harsh word stirs up anger. Proverbs 15:1

Day 2: Can you figure out which words are missing? Read the verse together 3x, then trace it and copy below.

A _____ answer turns away wrath, _____ harsh word stirs up anger. Proverbs 15:1

Day 3: More missing words! Can you recite the verse without help? Say the verse together 3x; then trace and copy below.

___ ___ answer turns away wrath, ___ __ harsh word stirs __ anger.
Proverbs 15:1

Day 4: Can you say the verse without help today? Fill in all the missing words, trace, and copy the verse below.

_____ _____ _____ answer _____

_____ wrath, _____ _ harsh

_____ stirs _____ anger.

Proverbs 15:1

_____

_____

_____

_____

_____

_____

_____

_____

A soft answer turns away wrath, but a harsh word stirs up anger. A soft answer turns away wrath, but a harsh word stirs up anger. A soft answer turns away wrath, but a harsh word stirs up anger. A soft answer turns away wrath, but a harsh word stirs up anger. A soft answer turns away wrath, but a harsh word stirs up anger. A soft answer turns away wrath, but a harsh word stirs up anger. A soft answer turns away wrath, but a harsh word stirs up anger. A soft answer turns away wrath, but a harsh word stirs up anger. A soft answer turns away wrath, but a harsh word stirs up anger. A soft answer turns away wrath, but a harsh word stirs up anger. A soft answer turns away wrath, but a harsh word stirs up anger. A soft answer turns away wrath, but a harsh word stirs up anger.

Day 5

No Copy Work!

Recite Proverbs 15:1 for family & friends

Color or highlight the verse picture, then tear it out
and display it somewhere you'll see it often

Write out Proverbs 15:1 on a memory card
(or use the free printable cards at writetheword.com)
and add it to your memory stack

Review the cards in your memory pile

A soft answer turns away wrath, but a harsh word stirs up anger. A soft answer turns away wrath, but a harsh word stirs up anger. A soft answer turns away wrath, but a harsh word stirs up anger. A soft answer turns away wrath, but a harsh word stirs up anger. A soft answer turns away wrath, but a harsh word stirs up anger. A soft answer turns away wrath, but a harsh word stirs up anger. A soft answer turns away wrath, but a harsh word stirs up anger. A soft answer turns away wrath, but a harsh word stirs up anger. A soft answer turns away wrath, but a harsh word stirs up anger. A soft answer turns away wrath, but a harsh word stirs up anger. A soft answer turns away wrath, but a harsh word stirs up anger. A soft answer turns away wrath, but a harsh word stirs up anger. A

A *soft* answer turns away wrath but a harsh word stirs up anger

Proverbs 15:1

Psalm 34:13

Keep your tongue from evil and your lips from speaking deceit

Day 1: New week, new verse! Read the verse together 3x, then trace it, and copy below.

Keep your tongue from evil and your lips from speaking deceit.

Psalm 34:13

Day 2: Can you figure out which words are missing? Read the verse together 3x, then trace it and copy below.

Keep your tongue ____
evil and your lips ____
speaking deceit.
Psalm 34:13

Day 3: More missing words! Can you recite the verse without help? Say the verse together 3x; then trace and copy below.

Keep _____ tongue _____

evil and _____ _____ _____

speaking deceit.

Psalm 34:13

Day 4: Can you say the verse without help today? Fill in all the missing words, trace, and copy the verse below.

_____ _____ tongue _____

evil _____ _____ _____

speaking deceit.

Psalm 34:13

Keep your tongue from evil and your lips from speaking deceit. Keep your tongue from evil and your lips from speaking deceit. Keep your tongue from evil and your lips from speaking deceit. Keep your tongue from evil and your lips from speaking deceit. Keep your tongue from evil and your lips from speaking deceit. Keep your tongue from evil and your lips from speaking deceit. Keep your tongue from evil and your lips from speaking deceit. Keep your tongue from evil and your lips from speaking deceit. Keep your tongue from evil and your lips from speaking deceit. Keep your tongue from evil and

Day 5

No Copy Work!

Recite Psalm 34:13 for family & friends

Color or highlight the verse picture, then tear it out
and display it somewhere you'll see it often

Write out Psalm 34:13 on a memory card
(or use the free printable cards at writetheword.com)
and add it to your memory stack

Review the cards in your memory pile

from evil and your lips from speaking deceit. Keep your tongue from evil and your lips from speaking deceit. Keep your tongue from evil and your lips from speaking deceit. Keep your tongue from evil and your lips from speaking deceit. Keep your tongue from evil and your lips from speaking deceit. Keep your tongue from evil and your lips from speaking deceit. Keep your tongue from evil and your lips from speaking deceit. Keep your tongue from evil and your lips from speaking deceit. Keep your tongue from evil and your lips from speaking deceit. Keep your tongue from evil and your lips from speaking deceit. Keep your tongue from evil and your lips from speaking deceit. Keep your tongue from evil and your lips from speaking deceit. Keep your tongue from evil and

Keep
your tongue
from
evil
and your lips
from
speaking
deceit

Psalm 34:13

1 Thessalonians 5:11

Therefore encourage one another and build one another up, just as you are doing

Day 1: New week, new verse! Read the verse together 3x, then trace it, and copy below.

therefore encourage
one another and build
one another up, just as
you are doing.
I Thessalonians 5:11

Day 2: Can you figure out which words are missing? Read the verse together 3x, then trace it and copy below.

therefore _____ encourage

_____ another and build

_____ another _____, just as

you are doing.

I Thessalonians 5:11

_____

- -

_____

- -

_____

- -

_____

- -

_____

- -

Day 3: More missing words! Can you recite the verse without help? Say the verse together 3x; then trace and copy below.

Therefore _____ encourage

_____ another _____ build

_____ another _____, just _____

you _____ doing.

I Thessalonians 5:11

Day 4: Can you say the verse without help today? Fill in all the missing words, trace, and copy the verse below.

Therefore _____ encourage _____ another _____ build _____ another _____, _____ _____ _____ doing.

I Thessalonians 5:11

_____

_____

_____

_____

_____

_____

_____

_____

Therefore encourage one another and build one another up, just as you are doing. Therefore encourage one another and build one another up, just as you are doing. Therefore encourage one another and build one another up, just as you are doing. Therefore encourage one another and build one another up, just as you are doing. Therefore encourage one another and build one another up, just as you are doing. Therefore encourage one another and build one another up, just as you are doing. Therefore encourage one another and build one another up, just as you are doing. Therefore encourage one another and build one another up, just as you are doing. Therefore encourage one another and build one another up, just as you are doing.

Day 5

No Copy Work!

Recite 1 Thessalonians 5:11 for family & friends

Color or highlight the verse picture, then tear it out and display it somewhere you'll see it often

Write out 1 Thessalonians 5:11 on a memory card (or use the free printable cards at writetheword.com) and add it to your memory stack

Review the cards in your memory pile

another and build one another up, just as you are doing. Therefore encourage one another and build one another up, just as you are doing. Therefore encourage one another and build one another up, just as you are doing. Therefore encourage one another and build one another up, just as you are doing. Therefore encourage one another and build one another up, just as you are doing. Therefore encourage one another and build one another up, just as you are doing. Therefore encourage one another and build one another up, just as you are doing. Therefore encourage one another and build one another up, just as you are doing. Therefore encourage one another and build one another up, just as you are doing. Therefore encourage one another and build one another up, just as you are doing. Therefore encourage one another and build one another up, just as you are doing. Therefore encourage one another and build one another up, just as you are doing. Therefore encourage one another and build one another up, just as you are doing Therefore

Therefore

encourage

one another

and

build

one another up

just as you

are doing

1 Thessalonians 5:11

Psalm 19:14*

Let the words of my mouth and the meditation of my heart be acceptable in your sight, O Lord

Day 1: New week, new verse! Read the verse together 3x, then trace it, and copy below.

Let the words of

my mouth and the

meditation of my heart

be acceptable in your

sight, O Lord.

Psalm 19:14

Day 2: Can you figure out which words are missing? Read the verse together 3x, then trace it and copy below.

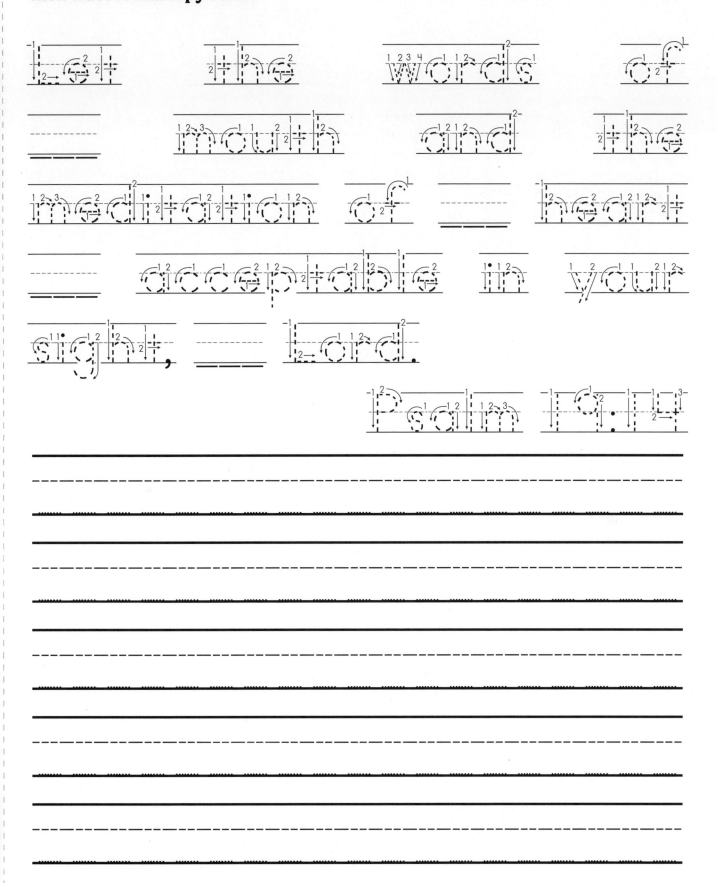

Let the words of ___ mouth and the meditation of ___ heart ___ acceptable in your sight, ___ Lord. Psalm 19:14

Day 3: More missing words! Can you recite the verse without help? Say the verse together 3x; then trace and copy below.

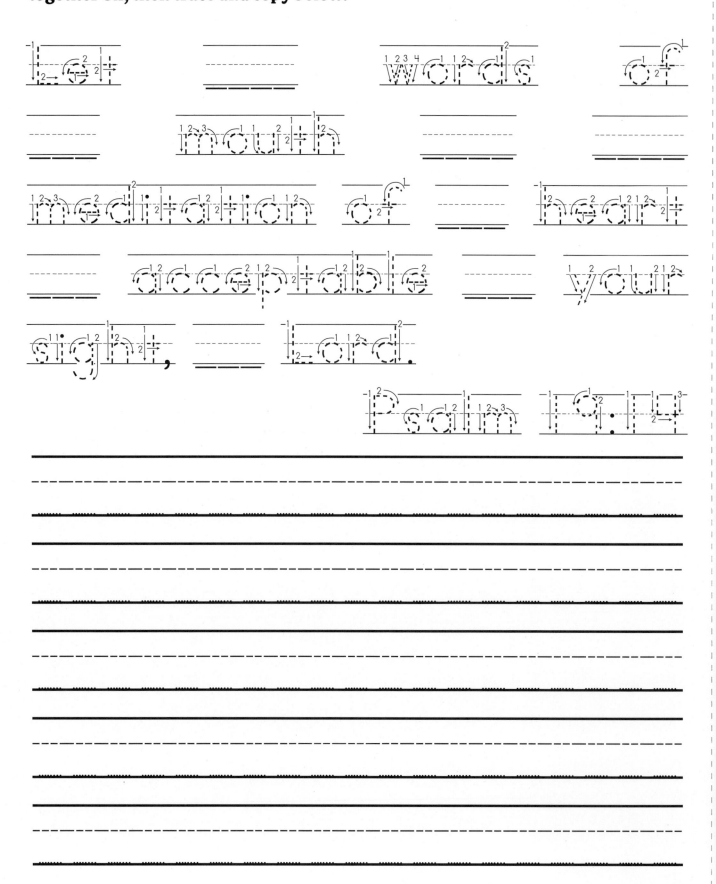

Let ___ words of ___ mouth ___ meditation of ___ heart ___ acceptable ___ your sight, ___ Lord. Psalm 19:14

Day 4: Can you say the verse without help today? Fill in all the missing words, trace, and copy the verse below.

_____ _____ words _____

_____ mouth _____

meditation _____ heart

acceptable _____ _____

sight, ___ Lord.

Psalm 19:14

_____

_____

_____

_____

_____

_____

_____

_____

Let the words of my mouth and the meditation of my heart be acceptable in your sight, O Lord, my rock and my redeemer. Let the words of my mouth and the meditation of my heart be acceptable in your sight, O Lord, my rock and my redeemer. Let the words of my mouth and the meditation of my heart be acceptable in your sight, O Lord, my rock and my redeemer. Let the words of my mouth and the meditation of my heart be acceptable in your sight, O Lord, my rock and my redeemer. Let the words of my mouth and the meditation of my heart be acceptable in your sight, O Lord, my rock and my redeemer. Let the words of my mouth and the meditation of my heart be acceptable in your sight, O Lord, my rock and my redeemer. Let the words of my mouth and the meditation of my heart be acceptable in your

Day 5

No Copy Work!

Recite Psalm 19:14* for family & friends

Color or highlight the verse picture, then tear it out and display it somewhere you'll see it often

Write out Psalm 19:14 on a memory card
(or use the free printable cards at writetheword.com)
and add it to your memory stack

Review the cards in your memory pile

my rock and my redeemer. Let the words of my mouth and the meditation of my heart be acceptable in your sight, O Lord, my rock and my redeemer. Let the words of my mouth and the meditation of my heart be acceptable in your sight, O Lord, my rock and my redeemer. Let the words of my mouth and the meditation of my heart be acceptable in your sight, O Lord, my rock and my redeemer. Let the words of my mouth and the meditation of my heart be acceptable in your sight, O Lord, my rock and my redeemer. Let the words of my mouth and the meditation of my heart be acceptable in your sight, O Lord, my rock and my redeemer. Let the words of my mouth and the meditation of my heart be acceptable in your sight, O Lord, my rock and my redeemer. Let the words of my mouth and the meditation of my heart be acceptable in your

Let the words of my mouth and the meditation of my heart be acceptable in your sight O, Lord

Psalm 19:14

SECTION SEVEN:
Our Conduct

WEEK FIFTEEN: Philippians 2:14—*Do all things without grumbling or disputing.*

WEEK SIXTEEN: Colossians 3:23—*Whatever you do, work heartily, as for the Lord and not for men.*

WEEK SEVENTEEN: James 1:19—*Let every person be quick to hear, slow to speak, slow to anger.*

WEEK EIGHTEEN: Luke 6:31—*Treat others the same way you want them to treat you.* (NASB)

WEEK NINETEEN: Ephesians 4:32—*Be kind to one another, tenderhearted, forgiving one another, as God in Christ forgave you.*

WEEK TWENTY: John 15:12—*This is my commandment, that you love one another as I have loved you.*

How does God want us to act? Be kind, do your work heartily, avoid arguments, don't complain, love and forgive each other, etc. These aren't just good morals, this is the example Christ set for us, and the life we're called to as Christians. Are they cleaning the bathroom lazily or heartily? Are they grumbling when you give them something to do? Are they speaking with kindness to Sally? Can they forgive when Jimmy grabbed their toy? These verses are shared with the hope to write God's standard on their hearts.

As you encourage your children to keep these commands, *remember, they will fail*. But just as God gave us the law to point us to Christ (see Galatians 3), so also, we can use his commands to point our children to the Lord. When they fail, let it be a point of discussion, and seek to direct their hearts to Christ, to come to him for help and grace to "fulfill" the requirement that is asked of them.

One further note: as you encourage your children, remember: *we often give our children their first impression of God, and at times, represent him to our children*. Just as we should run to God in our failures and inabilities, so also our children should learn (at least in the beginning) to run to us. Several years back, my husband taught our children to "ask for grace," if they felt overwhelmed by a task. We often use the term "grace" to excuse our failures when we mess up: "Oh, thank God for his grace." While there is some truth to this, "grace upon grace" is *God giving us the ability to do something that we could not do without him.* (See John 1:16.) It is a coming alongside. It is help. It is Christ in us, giving us the ability to will and work and to act when we ourselves are without strength (see Philippians 2:13). It is Paul's "But by God's grace, I am what I am" (see 1 Corinthians 15:10). To this day, when our youngest feels overwhelmed by his messy floor, he often calls, "Moommmmmy, can I have some grace?" His call for help is a welcome reminder to both of us. For my son, it teaches him to be humble, and to ask for help. For me, his cry for grace reminds my heart of the many times God has extended help to me in my time of need, encouraging me to do the same for him.

As you begin to go through these verses with your children, hold up the standard of the word, and show them God's requirement. But if they fall short (and they will), encourage them to call for help. And be willing, just as our Father has helped us, to come alongside with some extra "grace" for them.

Thoughts for Further Discussion and Study:

- Lead a child to pray through one of these situations they find it impossible to do.
- Encourage your children to ask for help if they find something too difficult.
- Why is it helpful to do your work heartily? To be kind? To forgive? How can this change our relationship with our brothers and sisters now? In the future?
- Are these commands from a harsh taskmaster who is being hard on us? Or are they commands from a Father who loves us and wants what is best?

Philippians 2:14

Do all things without grumbling or disputing

Day 1: New week, new verse! Read the verse together 3x, then trace it, and copy below.

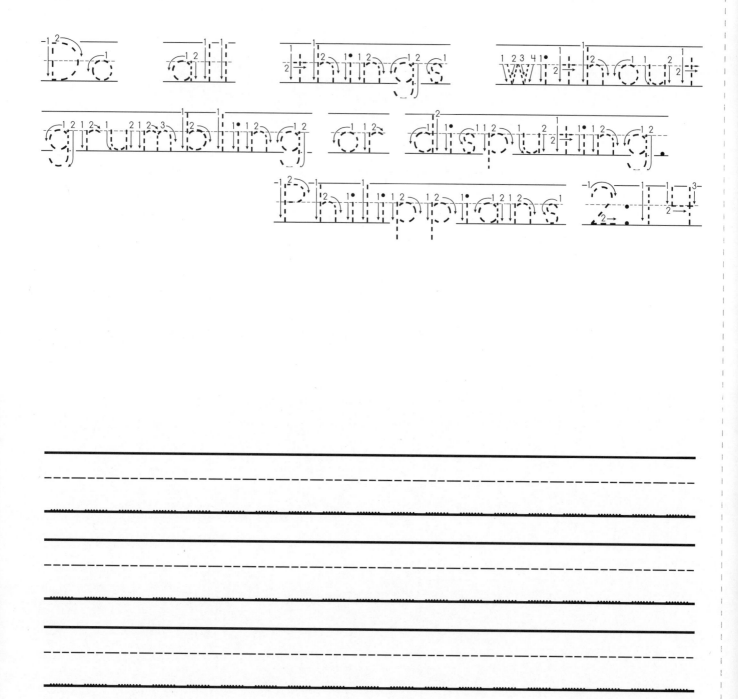

Do all things without grumbling or disputing. Philippians 2:14

Day 2: Can you figure out which words are missing? Read the verse together 3x, then trace it and copy below.

Do ___ things without grumbling or disputing. Philippians 2:14

Day 3: More missing words! Can you recite the verse without help? Say the verse together 3x; then trace and copy below.

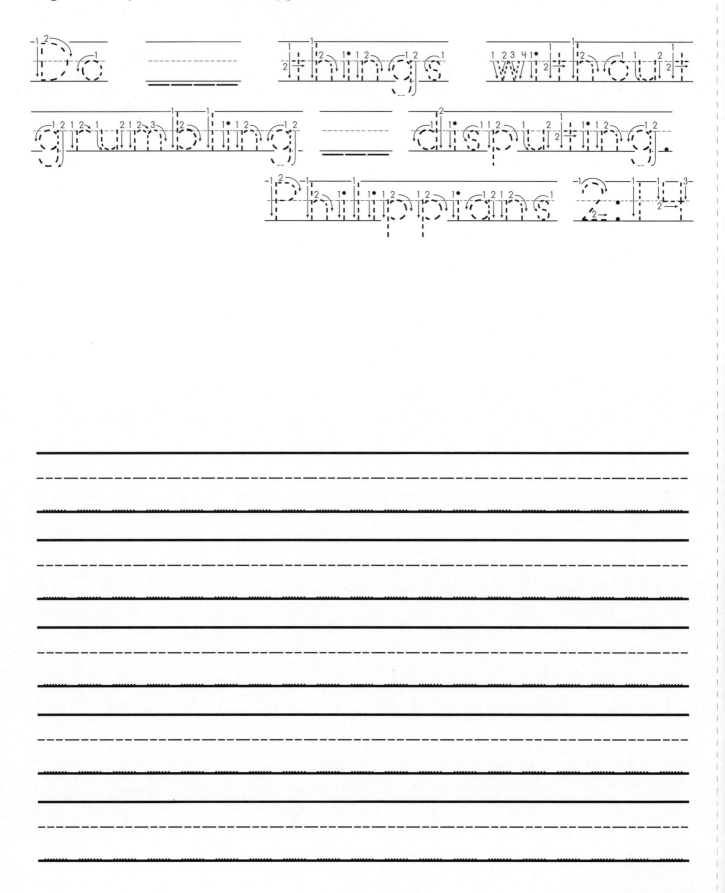

Do ___ things without grumbling ___ disputing. Philippians 2:14

Day 4: Can you say the verse without help today? Fill in all the missing words, trace, and copy the verse below.

_____ _____ _____ _____ without

grumbling __ disputing.

Philippians 2:14

Day 5

No Copy Work!

Recite Philippians 2:14 for family & friends

Color or highlight the verse picture, then tear it out
and display it somewhere you'll see it often

Write out Philippians 2:14 on a memory card
(or use the free printable cards at writetheword.com)
and add it to your memory stack

Review the cards in your memory pile

Do all things *without* grumbling or disputing

Philippians 2:14

Colossians 3:23

Whatever you do, work heartily, as for the Lord and not for men

Day 1: New week, new verse! Read the verse together 3x, then trace it, and copy below.

Whatever you do, work heartily, as for the Lord and not for men.
Colossians 3:23

Day 2: Can you figure out which words are missing? Read the verse together 3x, then trace it and copy below.

Whatever ____ do, work heartily, as ____ the Lord and not ____ men.
Colossians 3:23

Day 3: More missing words! Can you recite the verse without help? Say the verse together 3x; then trace and copy below.

Whatever _____ do, work heartily, as _____ the _____ _____ not _____ _____. Colossians 3:23

Day 4: Can you say the verse without help today? Fill in all the missing words, trace, and copy the verse below.

Whatever _____ _____, work

heartily, as _____ _____ _____

_____ _____ _____ _____ _____.

Colossians 3:23

Whatever you do, work heartily, as for the Lord and not for men. Whatever you do, work heartily, as for the Lord and not for men. Whatever you do, work heartily, as for the Lord and not for men. Whatever you do, work heartily, as for the Lord and not for men. Whatever you do, work heartily, as for the Lord and not for men. Whatever you do, work heartily, as for the Lord and not for men. Whatever you do, work heartily, as for the Lord and not for men. Whatever you do, work heartily, as for the Lord and not for men.

Day 5

No Copy Work!

Recite Colossians 3:23 for family & friends

Color or highlight the verse picture, then tear it out and display it somewhere you'll see it often

Write out Colossians 3:23 on a memory card (or use the free printable cards at writetheword.com) and add it to your memory stack

Review the cards in your memory pile

for the Lord and not for men. Whatever you do, work heartily, as for the Lord and not for men. Whatever you do, work heartily, as for the Lord and not for men. Whatever you do, work heartily, as for the Lord and not for men. Whatever you do, work heartily, as for the Lord and not for men. Whatever you do, work heartily, as for the Lord and not for men. Whatever you do, work heartily, as for the Lord and not for men. Whatever you do, work heartily, as for the Lord and not for men. Whatever you do, work heartily, as for the Lord and not for men. Whatever you do, work heartily, as for the Lord and not for men. Whatever you do, work heartily, as for the Lord and not for men. Whatever you do, work heartily, as

Whatever
you do
work
H E A R T I L Y
as for the
Lord
and not for
men

Colossians 3:23

James 1:19*

Let every person be quick to hear, slow to speak, slow to anger

Day 1: New week, new verse! Read the verse together 3x, then trace it, and copy below.

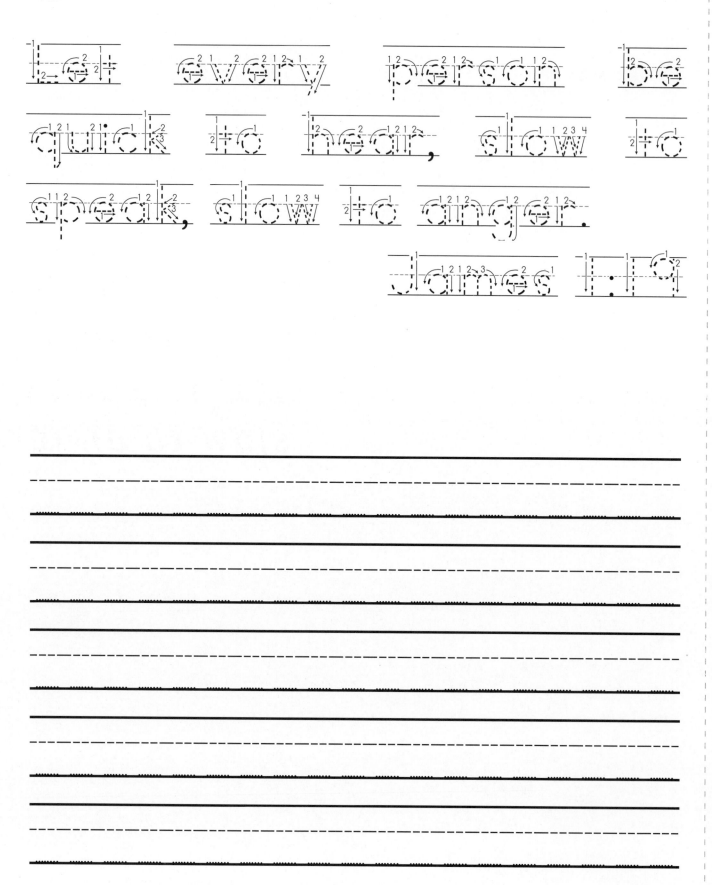

Let every person be quick to hear, slow to speak, slow to anger. James 1:19

Day 2: Can you figure out which words are missing? Read the verse together 3x, then trace it and copy below.

Let every person be quick ___ hear, slow ___ speak, slow ___ anger. James 1:9

Day 3: More missing words! Can you recite the verse without help? Say the verse together 3x; then trace and copy below.

_____ _____ every person _____
quick _____ hear, slow _____
speak, slow _____ anger.
James 1:9

Day 4: Can you say the verse without help today? Fill in all the missing words, trace, and copy the verse below.

_____ every person _____

quick __ hear, ____ _

speak, ____ __ __ anger.

James 1:19

Know this, my beloved brothers: let every person be quick to hear, slow to speak, slow to anger. Know this, my beloved brothers: let every person be quick to hear, slow to speak, slow to anger. Know this, my beloved brothers: let every person be quick to hear, slow to speak, slow to anger. Know this, my beloved brothers: let every person be quick to hear, slow to speak, slow to anger. Know this, my beloved brothers: let every person be quick to hear, slow to speak, slow to anger. Know this, my beloved brothers: let every person be quick to hear, slow to speak, slow to anger. Know this, my beloved brothers: let every person be quick to hear, slow to speak, slow to anger.

Day 5

No Copy Work!

Recite James 1:19* for family & friends

Color or highlight the verse picture, then tear it out
and display it somewhere you'll see it often

Write out James 1:19 on a memory card
(or use the free printable cards at writetheword.com)
and add it to your memory stack

Review the cards in your memory pile

Know this, my beloved brothers: let every person be quick to hear, slow to speak, slow to anger. Know this, my beloved brothers: let every person be quick to hear, slow to speak, slow to anger. Know this, my beloved brothers: let every person be quick to hear, slow to speak, slow to anger. Know this, my beloved brothers: let every person be quick to hear, slow to speak, slow to anger. Know this, my beloved brothers: let every person be quick to hear, slow to speak, slow to anger. Know this, my beloved brothers: let every person be quick to hear, slow to speak, slow to anger. Know this, my beloved brothers: let every person be quick to

LET EVERY PERSON BE

quick to

hear

slow to

speak

slow to

anger

James 1:19

Luke 6:31

Treat others the same way you want them to treat you

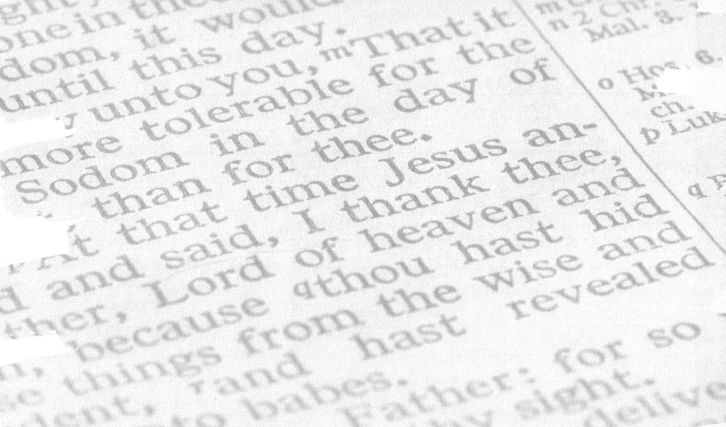

Day 1: New week, new verse! Read the verse together 3x, then trace it, and copy below.

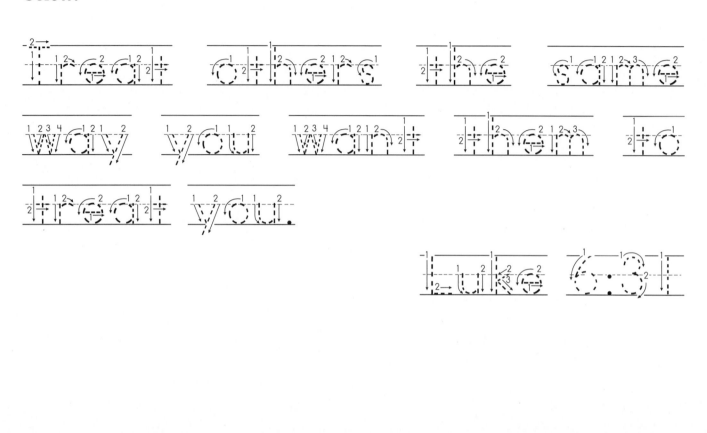

Treat others the same way you want them to treat you.

Luke 6:31

- -

- -

- -

- -

- -

Day 2: Can you figure out which words are missing? Read the verse together 3x, then trace it and copy below.

treat others ___ same way you want them ___ treat you.

Luke 6:31

Day 3: More missing words! Can you recite the verse without help? Say the verse together 3x; then trace and copy below.

treat others _____ same
way _____ want them _____
treat _____.

Luke 6:31

Day 4: Can you say the verse without help today? Fill in all the missing words, trace, and copy the verse below.

treat others _____ same

treat _____.

Luke 6:31

Day 5

No Copy Work!

Recite Luke 6:31 for family & friends

Color or highlight the verse picture, then tear it out
and display it somewhere you'll see it often

Write out Luke 6:31 on a memory card
(or use the free printable cards at writetheword.com)
and add it to your memory stack

Review the cards in your memory pile

Treat
others
the same way
you
want them
to treat
you

Luke 6:31

Ephesians 4:32

Be kind to one another, tenderhearted, forgiving one another, as God in Christ forgave you

Day 1: New week, new verse! Read the verse together 3x, then trace it, and copy below.

Be kind to one another, tenderhearted, forgiving one another, as God in Christ forgave you. Ephesians 4:32

Day 2: Can you figure out which words are missing? Read the verse together 3x, then trace it and copy below.

Be kind to _____ another,
tenderhearted,   forgiving _____ another,   as
God in Christ forgave
_____.

Ephesians 4:32

_____
_____
_____
_____
_____
_____
_____
_____
_____

Day 3: More missing words! Can you recite the verse without help? Say the verse together 3x; then trace and copy below.

Be kind ____ ____ another, tenderhearted, for giving ____ another, ____ God ____ Christ forgave ____.

Ephesians 4:32

Day 4: Can you say the verse without help today? Fill in all the missing words, trace, and copy the verse below.

_____ kind _____ _____ another,
tenderhearted, for
giving another, _____
_____ _____ Christ forgave
_____ _____.

Ephesians 4:32

Be kind to one another, tenderhearted, forgiving one another, as God in Christ forgave you. Be kind to one another, tenderhearted, forgiving one another, as God in Christ forgave you. Be kind to one another, tenderhearted, forgiving one another, as God in Christ forgave you. Be kind to one another, tenderhearted, forgiving one another, as God in Christ forgave you. Be kind to one another, tenderhearted, forgiving one another, as God in Christ forgave you. Be kind to one another, tenderhearted, forgiving one another,

Day 5

No Copy Work!

Recite Ephesians 5:32 for family & friends

Color or highlight the verse picture, then tear it out
and display it somewhere you'll see it often

Write out Ephesians 4:32 on a memory card
(or use the free printable cards at writetheword.com)
and add it to your memory stack

Review the cards in your memory pile

as God in Christ forgave you. Be kind to one another, tenderhearted, forgiving one another, as God in Christ forgave you. Be kind to one another, tenderhearted, forgiving one another, as God in Christ forgave you. Be kind to one another, tenderhearted, forgiving one another, as God in Christ forgave you. Be kind to one another, tenderhearted, forgiving one another, as God in Christ forgave you. Be kind to one another, tenderhearted, forgiving one another, as God in Christ forgave you. Be kind to one another, tenderhearted, forgiving one another, as God in Christ forgave you. Be kind to one another, tenderhearted, forgiving

Be kind to one another TENDERHEARTED forgiving one another as GOD in Christ FORGAVE you

Ephesians 4:32

John 15:12

This is my commandment, that you love one another as I have loved you

Day 1: New week, new verse! Read the verse together 3x, then trace it, and copy below.

This is my commandment, that you love one another as I have loved you.

John 15:12

Day 2: Can you figure out which words are missing? Read the verse together 3x, then trace it and copy below.

This is ___ commandment, that ___ love one another ___ I have loved ___.

John 15:12

Day 3: More missing words! Can you recite the verse without help? Say the verse together 3x; then trace and copy below.

_____ _____ _____ commandment,

that _____ love one

another _____ _____ have

loved _____.

John 15:12

Day 4: Can you say the verse without help today? Fill in all the missing words, trace, and copy the verse below.

_____ = = commandment,

_____ = love _____

another = = have

loved _____.

John 15:12

Day 5

No Copy Work!

Recite John 15:12 for family & friends

Color or highlight the verse picture, then tear it out
and display it somewhere you'll see it often

Write out John 15:12 on a memory card
(or use the free printable cards at writetheword.com)
and add it to your memory stack

Review the cards in your memory pile

This is my commandment that you love one another as I have loved you

John 15:12

SECTION EIGHT:
God's Heart toward Us

WEEK TWENTY-ONE: Romans 8:31—*What then shall we say to these things? If God is for us, who can be against us?*

WEEK TWENTY-TWO: 1 John 3:16—*By this we know love, that he laid down his life for us, and we ought to lay down our lives for the brothers.*

WEEK TWENTY-THREE: Romans 5:8—*But God shows his love for us in that while we were still sinners, Christ died for us.*

As we learn about conduct and how the Lord desires us to act (and as we fail, and realize we can't keep God's standard), it is important to be reminded of God's heart towards us. No matter how many times our children mess up, God is for them. He loves them, and he went to the cross and shed his blood to make them clean. Our children should know, through and through that God's love for them is full, complete, unwavering, unconditional, and *never as a result of their good works* (Titus 3:5, Ephesians 2:8-10). Yes, as we discover his love more and more, our heart's response is to return and serve him with our whole heart, but this should be our *response* to God's love, not the way we receive it.

Thoughts for Further Discussion and Study:

- The gospel. You don't need to lead a young child to the Lord and assure them of salvation, but you can begin to explain how it works as you continue to encourage them to call upon him and come to him.
- God loved us so much that he laid down his life and died for us. This is God's picture of love to us. What does that mean about how we show love and kindness to others?
- Did God die for us because we did good things?

Romans 8:31

*What then shall we say
to these things?
If God is for us,
who can be against us?*

Day 1: New week, new verse! Read the verse together 3x, then trace it, and copy below.

What then shall we say to these things? If God is for us, who can be against us?

Romans 8:31

Day 2: Can you figure out which words are missing? Read the verse together 3x, then trace it and copy below.

What then shall ___ say to these things? If God is ___ ___, who can be against ___?

Romans 8:31

Day 3: More missing words! Can you recite the verse without help? Say the verse together 3x; then trace and copy below.

What then shall ___ say to these things? If ___ is ___ ___, who ___ ___ against ___ ?

Romans 8:31

Day 4: Can you say the verse without help today? Fill in all the missing words, trace, and copy the verse below.

What then shall _____ _____ _____ these things? If _____ _____ _____ _____ _____, who _____ _____ against _____ _____?

Romans 8:31

What then shall we say to these things? If God is for us, who can be against us? What then shall we say to these things? If God is for us, who can be against us? What then shall we say to these things? If God is for us, who can be against us? What then shall we say to these things? If God is for us, who can be against us? What then shall we say to these things? If God is for us, who can be against us? What then shall we say to these things? If God is for us, who can be against us? What then shall we say to these things? If God is for us, who can be against us? What then shall we say to these things? If God is for us, who can be against us? What then shall we say to these things? If

Day 5

No Copy Work!

Recite Romans 8:31 for family & friends

Color or highlight the verse picture, then tear it out and display it somewhere you'll see it often

Write out Romans 8:31 on a memory card
(or use the free printable cards at writetheword.com)
and add it to your memory stack

Review the cards in your memory pile

for us, who can be against us? What then shall we say to these things? If God is for us, who can be against us? What then shall we say to these things? If God is for us, who can be against us? What then shall we say to these things? If God is for us, who can be against us? What then shall we say to these things? If God is for us, who can be against us? What then shall we say to these things? If God is for us, who can be against us? What then shall we say to these things? If God is for us, who can be against us? What then shall we say to these things? If God is for us, who can be against us? What then shall we say to these things? If God is for us, who can be against us? What then shall we say to these things? If God is for us, who can be against us? What then shall we say to these things? If God is for us, who can be against

WHAT then
shall we say
to these things?
If **God** is
for us
WHO
can be
against us?

Romans 8:31

1 John 3:16

By this we know love, that he laid down his life for us, and we ought to lay down our lives for the brothers

Day 1: New week, new verse! Read the verse together 3x, then trace it, and copy below.

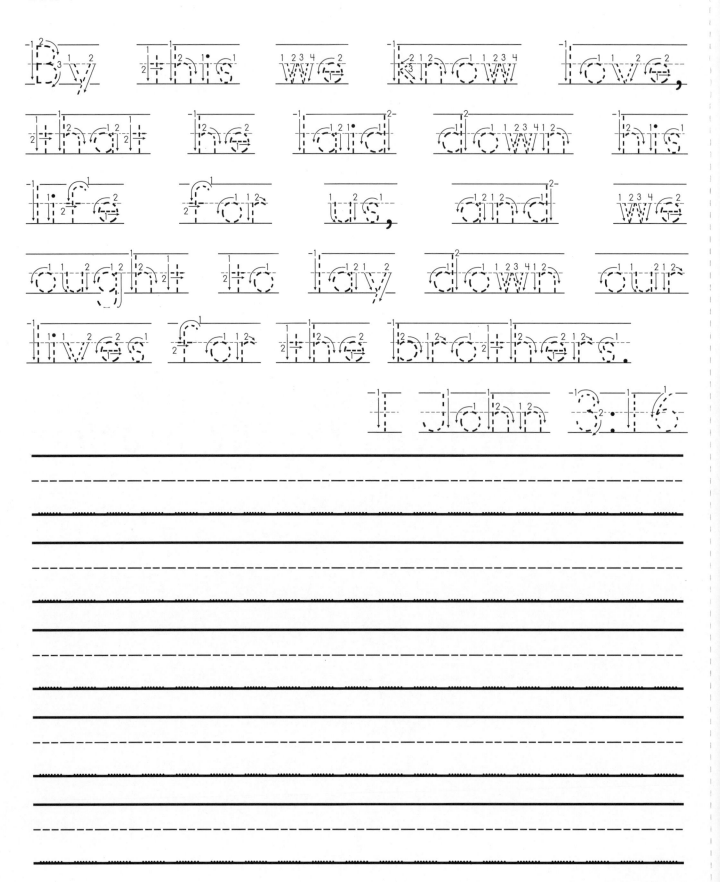

By this we know love, that he laid down his life for us, and we ought to lay down our lives for the brothers. I John 3:16

Day 2: Can you figure out which words are missing? Read the verse together 3x, then trace it and copy below.

By _____ we know love, that _____ laid down his life for _____, and we ought to lay down our lives _____ the brothers. I John 3:16

Day 3: More missing words! Can you recite the verse without help? Say the verse together 3x; then trace and copy below.

By _____ _____ know love, that _____ laid down his life _____ _____, and _____ ought _____ lay down our lives _____ _____ brothers.

I John 3:16

Day 4: Can you say the verse without help today? Fill in all the missing words, trace, and copy the verse below.

By this we know love, that he laid down his life for us, and we ought to lay down our lives for the brothers. By this we know love, that he laid down his life for us, and we ought to lay down our lives for the brothers. By this we know love, that he laid down his life for us, and we ought to lay down our lives for the brothers. By this we know love, that he laid down his life for us, and we ought to lay down our lives for the brothers. By this we know love, that he laid down his life for us, and we ought to lay down our lives for the brothers. By this we know love, that he laid down his life for us, and we ought to lay down our lives for the brothers.

Day 5

No Copy Work!

Recite 1 John 3:16 for family & friends

Color or highlight the verse picture, then tear it out and display it somewhere you'll see it often

Write out 1 John 3:16 on a memory card
(or use the free printable cards at writetheword.com)
and add it to your memory stack

Review the cards in your memory pile

brothers. By this we know love, that he laid down his life for us, and we ought to lay down our lives for the brothers. By this we know love, that he laid down his life for us, and we ought to lay down our lives for the brothers. By this we know love, that he laid down his life for us, and we ought to lay down our lives for the brothers. By this we know love, that he laid down his life for us, and we ought to lay down our lives for the brothers. By this we know love, that he laid down his life for us, and we ought to lay down our lives for the brothers. By this we know love, that he laid down his life for us, and we ought to lay down our lives for the brothers. By this we know love, that he laid down his life for us, and we ought to lay down our lives for the brothers. By this we know love, that he laid down his life for us, and we ought to lay down our lives for the

By this WE KNOW love that He LAID DOWN HIS life for us. And we ought TO LAY DOWN OUR lives for the brothers

1 John 3:16

Romans 5:8

But God shows his love for us in that while we were still sinners, Christ died for us

Day 1: New week, new verse! Read the verse together 3x, then trace it, and copy below.

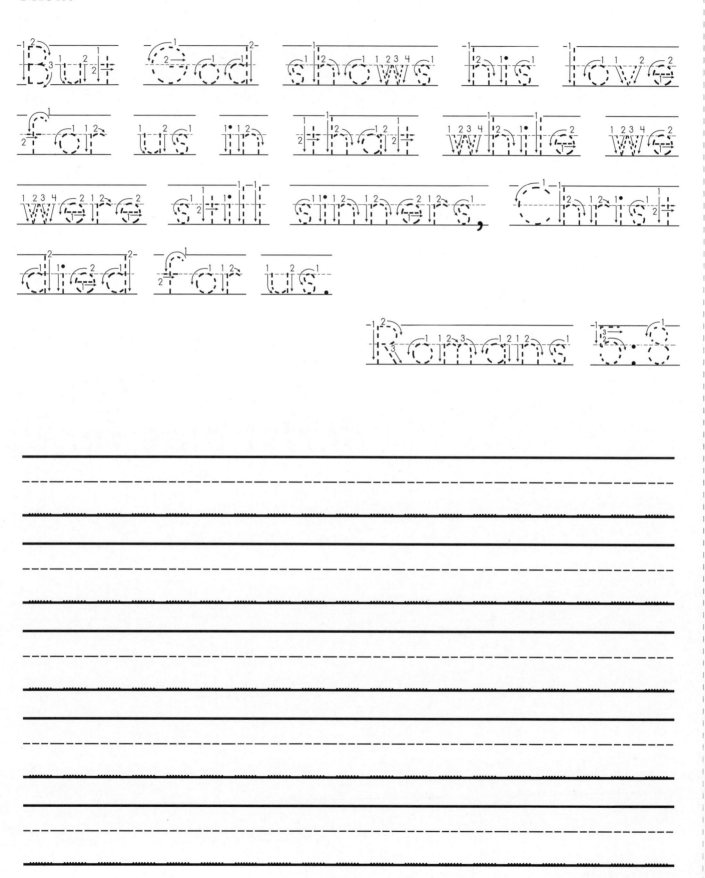

But God shows his love for us in that while we were still sinners, Christ died for us.

Romans 5:8

Day 2: Can you figure out which words are missing? Read the verse together 3x, then trace it and copy below.

But _____ _____ shows his love

for _____ in that while _____

were still sinners, Christ

died for _____.

Romans 5:8

Day 3: More missing words! Can you recite the verse without help? Say the verse together 3x; then trace and copy below.

But _____ _____ shows _____ love for _____ in _____ while _____ were still sinners, Christ died _____ _____.

Romans 5:8

Day 4: Can you say the verse without help today? Fill in all the missing words, trace, and copy the verse below.

____ ____ ____ shows ___ love

____ ____ ____ ____ while __

were ____ sinners,

Christ died ___ ___.

Romans 5:8

but God shows his love for us in that while we were still sinners, Christ died for us. but God shows his love for us in that while we were still sinners, Christ died for us. but God shows his love for us in that while we were still sinners, Christ died for us. but God shows his love for us in that while we were still sinners, Christ died for us. but God shows his love for us in that while we were still sinners, Christ died for us. but God shows his love for us in that while we were still sinners, Christ died for us. but God shows his love for us in that while we were still sinners, Christ died for us. but God shows his love for us in that while we were still sinners, Christ died for us. but God shows his love for us in that while we were still sinners, Christ died for us. but God shows his love for us in that while we were still sinners, Christ died for us. but God shows his love for us in that while we were still sinners, Christ died for us. but God shows his love for us in that while we were still sinners, Christ died for us. but God shows his love for us in that while we were still sinners, Christ died for us. but God shows his love for us in that while we were still sinners, Christ died for us. but God shows his love for us in that while we were still sinners, Christ died for us.

Day 5

No Copy Work!

Recite Romans 5:8 for family & friends

Color or highlight the verse picture, then tear it out and display it somewhere you'll see it often

Write out Romans 5:8 on a memory card
(or use the free printable cards at writetheword.com)
and add it to your memory stack

Review the cards in your memory pile

us in that while we were still sinners, Christ died for us. but God shows his love for us in that while we were still sinners, Christ died for us. but God shows his love for us in that while we were still sinners, Christ died for us. but God shows his love for us in that while we were still sinners, Christ died for us. but God shows his love for us in that while we were still sinners, Christ died for us. but God shows his love for us in that while we were still sinners, Christ died for us. but God shows his love for us in that while we were still sinners, Christ died for us. but God shows his love for us in that while we were still sinners, Christ died for us. but God shows his love for us in that while we were still sinners, Christ died for us. but God shows his love for us in that while we were still sinners, Christ died for us. but God shows his love for us in that while

But God
shows His
love for us
IN THAT
while we were
still sinners
CHRIST
DIED for us

Romans 5:8

SECTION NINE:

Learning to Trust God

WEEK TWENTY-FOUR: Philippians 4:13—*I can do all things through him who strengthens me.*

WEEK TWENTY-FIVE: 1 Peter 5:7—*Casting all your anxieties on him, because he cares for you.*

WEEK TWENTY-SIX: Proverbs 3:5—*Trust in the LORD with all your heart, and do not lean on your own understanding.*

WEEK TWENTY-SEVEN: Proverbs 3:6—*In all your ways acknowledge him, and he will make straight your paths.*

When we see how God loves us, when we see how he is for us, we begin to understand that God is trustworthy. Trust is formed and strengthened from a faith that is proven over and over. Answered prayers, provided needs, help in time of need, all assure a young child that God can be trusted. As a habit is formed to "cast their cares on the Lord," they will discover God can be trusted to handle our needs, our troubles, our day-to-day concerns, and even our sins. In all things, we can come to him. We can come to him to be made clean, we can come to him for help, we can come to him to direct our paths. A 6-,7-, or 8-year-old likely won't be seeking the Lord on their own yet, but these are good verses to memorize as they begin to cultivate the habit of entrusting problems and worries to him.

One further note: if your child can't or doesn't feel comfortable praying, don't force it—but *do* let them see the example of their parents praying. Throughout the gospels, *Jesus responds to the faith and prayer of the parent when he heals or helps their children*. So while we should ask our children if they want to pray and encourage them to do so, if you are in the midst of a family crisis or your child/children need help—let them see you coming to Christ on their behalf, stopping in the midst of the mess to cast your family's most difficult moments on him.

Thoughts for Further Discussion and Study:

- Do they have any "cares" they can cast on him? Bedtime prayers are a great way to work this lifelong lesson into your routine.

(over)

- What is a practical way they can "acknowledge him" in their ways?
- Look at the context of Philippians 4:13. Does this mean God can give us power to do anything? Or is there a deeper meaning here?
- If you have a family conflict this week or run into a problem that you can't solve, stop and pray, reminding your children of these verses as you do.

Philippians 4:13

I can do all things through him who strengthens me

Day 1: New week, new verse! Read the verse together 3x, then trace it, and copy below.

I can do all things through him who strengthens me. Philippians 4:13

Day 2: Can you figure out which words are missing? Read the verse together 3x, then trace it and copy below.

I can do ___ things through ___ him who strengthens ___.

Philippians 4:13

Day 3: More missing words! Can you recite the verse without help? Say the verse together 3x; then trace and copy below.

I _____ _____ _____ things

through _____ who

strengthens _____.

Philippians 4:13

Day 4: Can you say the verse without help today? Fill in all the missing words, trace, and copy the verse below.

things

through

strengthens .

Philippians 4:13

Day 5

No Copy Work!

Recite Philippians 4:13 for family & friends

Color or highlight the verse picture, then tear it out
and display it somewhere you'll see it often

Write out Philippians 4:13 on a memory card
(or use the free printable cards at writetheword.com)
and add it to your memory stack

Review the cards in your memory pile

I can do
ALL THINGS
through
Him
who
strengthens
me

Philippians 4:13

1 Peter 5:7

Casting all your anxieties on him, because he cares for you

Day 1: New week, new verse! Read the verse together 3x, then trace it, and copy below.

Casting all your anxieties on him, because he cares for you.

I Peter 5:7

Day 2: Can you figure out which words are missing? Read the verse together 3x, then trace it and copy below.

Casting all your

anxieties ___ ___,

because ___ cares for

you.

I Peter 5:7

Day 3: More missing words! Can you recite the verse without help? Say the verse together 3x; then trace and copy below.

Casting _____ your anxieties _____ _____, because _____ cares for _____.

1 Peter 5:7

Day 4: Can you say the verse without help today? Fill in all the missing words, trace, and copy the verse below.

Casting all your anxieties on him, because he cares for you. Casting all your anxieties on him, because he cares for you. Casting all your anxieties on him, because he cares for you. casting all your anxieties on him, because he cares for you. Casting all your anxieties on him, because he cares for you. Casting all your anxieties on him, because he cares for you. Casting all your anxieties on him, because he cares for you. Casting all your anxieties on him, because he cares for you. casting all your anxieties on him, because he cares for you. Casting all your anxieties on him, because he cares for you. Casting

Day 5

No Copy Work!

Recite 1 Peter 5:7 for family & friends

Color or highlight the verse picture, then tear it out and display it somewhere you'll see it often

Write out 1 Peter 5:7 on a memory card
(or use the free printable cards at writetheword.com)
and add it to your memory stack

Review the cards in your memory pile

because he cares for you. casting all your anxieties on him, because he cares for you. Casting all your anxieties on him, because he cares for you. Casting all your anxieties on him, because he cares for you. Casting all your anxieties on him, because he cares for you. Casting all your anxieties on him, because he cares for you. casting all your anxieties on him, because he cares for you. Casting all your anxieties on him, because he cares for you. Casting all your anxieties on him, because he cares for you. Casting all your anxieties on him, because he cares for you. Casting all your anxieties on him, because he cares for you. casting all your anxieties on him, because he cares for you. Casting all your anxieties on him, because he cares for you. Casting all your anxieties on him, because he cares for you. Casting

Casting all your anxieties on Him because He cares for you

1 Peter 5:7

Proverbs 3:5

Trust in the Lord with all your heart, and do not lean on your own understanding

Day 1: New week, new verse! Read the verse together 3x, then trace it, and copy below.

Trust in the Lord with all your heart, and do not lean on your own understanding.

Proverbs 3:5

Day 2: Can you figure out which words are missing? Read the verse together 3x, then trace it and copy below.

Trust _____ the Lord with _____ your heart, and do not lean _____ your own understanding.

Proverbs 3:5

Day 3: More missing words! Can you recite the verse without help? Say the verse together 3x; then trace and copy below.

Trust _____ _____ Lord with _____ your heart, and _____ _____ lean _____ your own understanding. Proverbs 3:5

Day 4: Can you say the verse without help today? Fill in all the missing words, trace, and copy the verse below.

Trust _____ _____ Lord _____

_____ _____ heart, _____ _____

_____ lean _____ _____ own

understanding.

Proverbs 3:5

Day 5

No Copy Work!

Recite Proverbs 3:5 for family & friends

Color or highlight the verse picture, then tear it out
and display it somewhere you'll see it often

Write out Proverbs 3:5 on a memory card
(or use the free printable cards at writetheword.com)
and add it to your memory stack

Review the cards in your memory pile

TRUST *in the*

Lord

with all your

heart,

and do not

LEAN

on your own

understanding

Proverbs 3:5

Proverbs 3:6

In all your ways, acknowledge him, and he will make straight your paths

Day 1: New week, new verse! Read the verse together 3x, then trace it, and copy below.

In all your ways acknowledge him, and he will make straight your paths.

Proverbs 3:6

Day 2: Can you figure out which words are missing? Read the verse together 3x, then trace it and copy below.

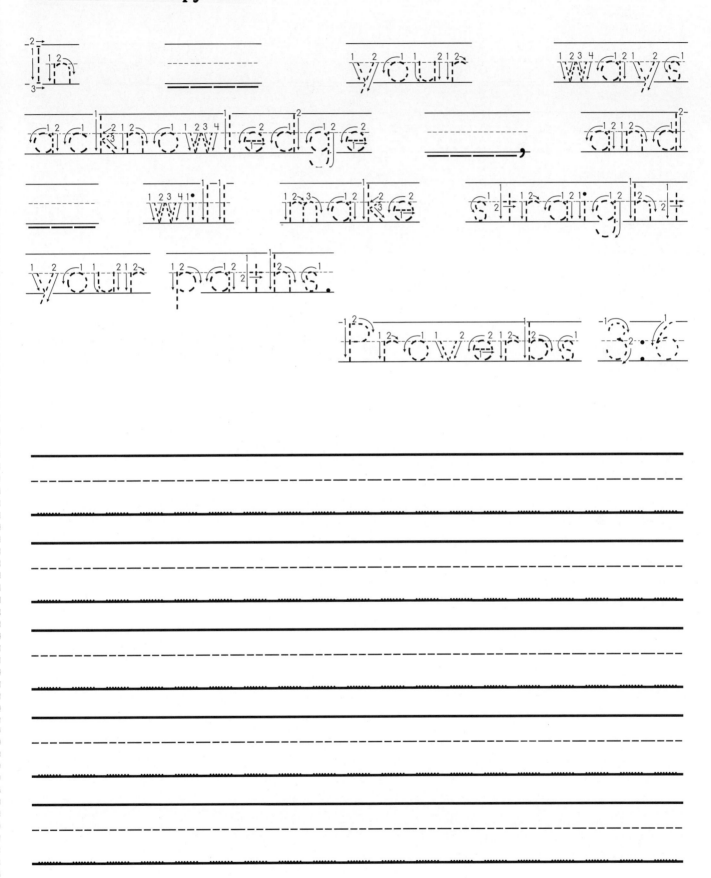

In _____ your ways

acknowledge _____, and

_____ will make straight

your paths.

Proverbs 3:6

Day 3: More missing words! Can you recite the verse without help? Say the verse together 3x; then trace and copy below.

In ____ ____ ____ ways acknowledge ____, and ____ will make straight ____ paths. Proverbs 3:6

Day 4: Can you say the verse without help today? Fill in all the missing words, trace, and copy the verse below.

_____ _____ _____ *ways*

acknowledge _____, _____ _____

_____ *make straight* _____

paths.

Proverbs 3:6

Trust in the Lord with all your heart, and do not lean on your own understanding. In all your ways acknowledge him, and he will make straight your paths. Trust in the Lord with all your heart, and do not lean on your own understanding. In all your ways acknowledge him, and he will make straight your paths. Trust in the Lord with all your heart, and do not lean on your own understanding. In all your ways acknowledge him, and he will make straight your paths. Trust in the Lord with all your heart, and do not lean on your own

Day 5

No Copy Work!

Recite Proverbs 3:5 and 6 for family & friends

Color or highlight the verse picture, then tear it out and display it somewhere you'll see it often

Write out Proverbs 3:6 on a memory card
(or use the free printable cards at writetheword.com)
and add it to your memory stack

Review the cards in your memory pile

your paths. Trust in the Lord with all your heart, and do not lean on your own understanding. In all your ways acknowledge him, and he will make straight your paths. Trust in the Lord with all your heart, and do not lean on your own understanding. In all your ways acknowledge him, and he will make straight your paths. Trust in the Lord with all your heart, and do not lean on your own understanding. In all your ways acknowledge him, and he will make straight your paths. Trust in the Lord with all your heart, and do not lean on your own understanding. In all your ways acknowledge him, and he will make straight your paths. Trust in the Lord with all your heart, and do not lean on your own understanding. In all your ways acknowledge him, and he will make straight your paths. Trust in the Lord with all your heart, and do not lean on your own

In all your ways
acknowledge
Him
and **He** will
make straight
your

P A T H S

Proverbs 3:6

SECTION TEN:
Our Heart

WEEK TWENTY-EIGHT: 1 Samuel 16:7—*For the L*ORD* sees not as man sees: man looks on the outward appearance, but the L*ORD* looks on the heart.*

WEEK TWENTY-NINE: Proverbs 23:26—*My son, give me your heart, and let your eyes observe† my ways.*

WEEK THIRTY: Psalm 119:11—*I have stored up† your word in my heart, that I might not sin against you.*

†alternate translation: "delight in"   †alternate translation: "hidden"

These final verses deal with the heart. The Bible says, "Even a child is known by his actions..." (see Proverbs 20:11). As parents, we want to train our children in the way of righteousness, especially while they are young. But it is important for them to know, even at a young age, that God is firstly, concerned with their heart. It is not only about doing the right thing, but about having the right heart. We can train actions, but the Lord must give us a willing heart. As a child learns what his actions should be, and begins to recognize that his heart doesn't always want to obey, this is a wonderful opportunity to encourage our children to come to the Lord, who sees the heart, and call out to him for help and forgiveness.

Our final verse, Psalm 119:11, is meant to be an encouragement. If you are finishing this first year of *Write the Word*, you have hidden his word in your heart. Praise the Lord! May the Lord use these materials to encourage, convict, and help you in your walk with him. Rejoice with your child, celebrate with your child. And stay in prayer, that the Lord will use these verses with your children for years to come.

Thoughts for Further Discussion and Study:

- Have they ever felt bad about doing something wrong? What did it feel like? What did they do about it? Explain to them that this is their conscience, and one of the areas of the heart where the Lord speaks. God has built this into our spirit to keep us on the right path. (see Isaiah 30:21, Romans 2:15)
- What does God see when he looks on their heart? Do they work willingly or grudgingly? Do they apologize, but stomp off? Do they say "okay," but then slam the door? Do our hearts match our actions? God sees all—and even more than the right actions, God is looking for the right heart.

Review the Year:

- Look back on the year together. Do they still have all 30 verses memorized?
- Can they remember a time this year when the Lord used one of their memorized verses to keep them from sinning or to encourage them?
- What about you, Mom and Dad? Share a story with your children about a time having the word in your heart kept you from sinning against him. Do you have any stories from this year?

1 Samuel 16:7*

For the Lord sees not as man sees: man looks on the outward appearance, but the Lord looks on the heart

Day 1: New week, new verse! Read the verse together 3x, then trace it, and copy below.

For the Lord sees not as man sees: man looks on the outward appearance, but the Lord looks on the heart. I Samuel 16:7

Day 2: Can you figure out which words are missing? Read the verse together 3x, then trace it and copy below.

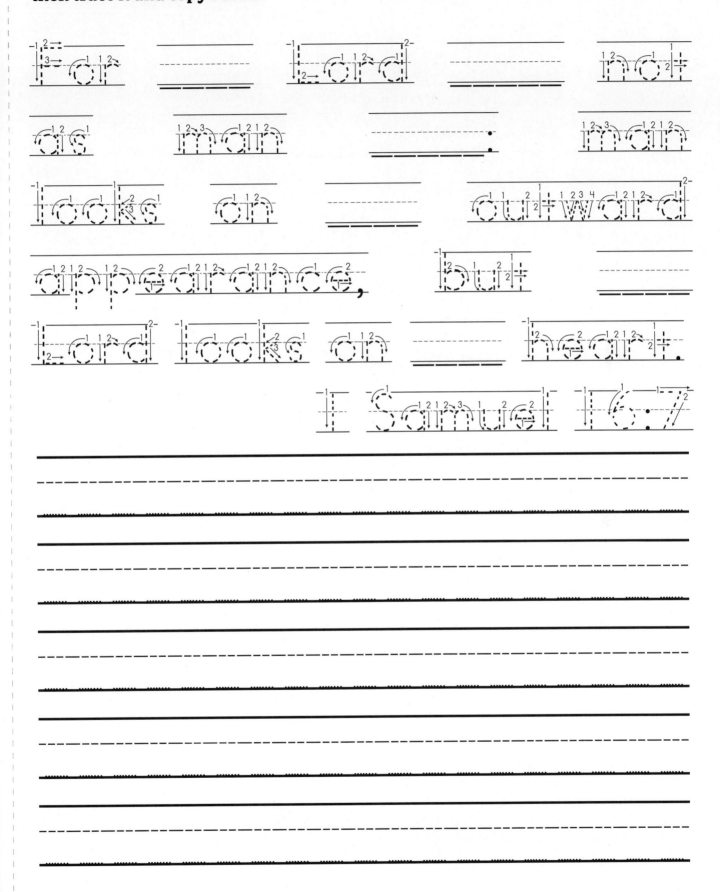

For _____ Lord _____ not as man _____ : man looks on _____ outward appearance, but _____ Lord looks on _____ heart. I Samuel 16:7

Day 3: More missing words! Can you recite the verse without help? Say the verse together 3x; then trace and copy below.

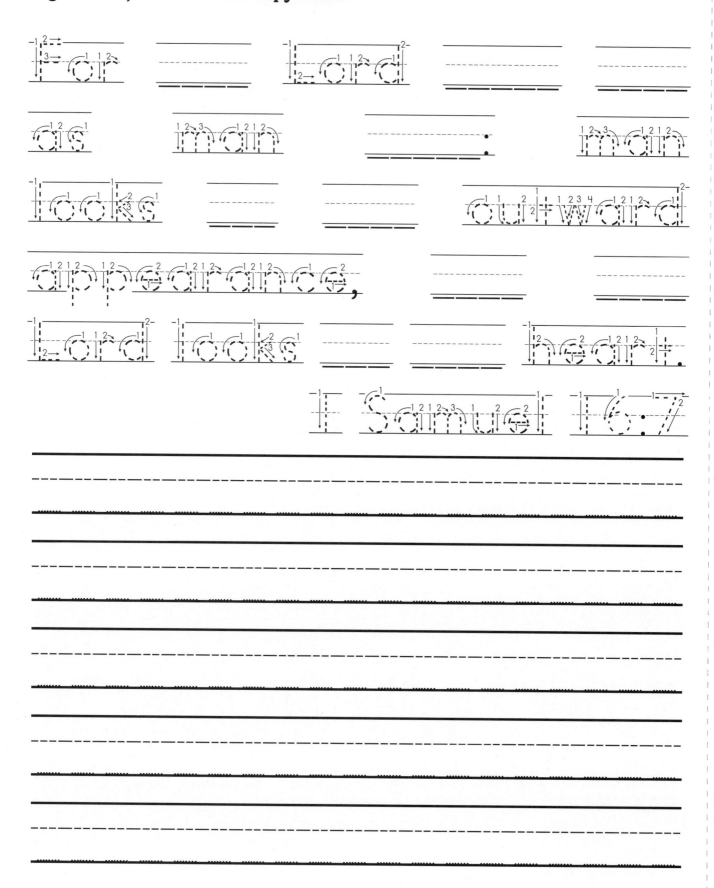

For ___ Lord ___ ___ as man ___ : man looks ___ ___ outward appearance, ___ ___ Lord looks ___ ___ ___ heart. I Samuel 16:7

Day 4: Can you say the verse without help today? Fill in all the missing words, trace, and copy the verse below.

_____   _____   Lord   _____   _____

_____   _____   _____   .

looks   _____   _____   outward

appearance,   _____   _____

Lord looks _____ _____ heart.

I Samuel 16:7

_____

_____

_____

_____

_____

_____

But the Lord said to Samuel, "Do not look on his appearance or on the height
of his stature, because I have rejected him. For the Lord sees not as man sees:
man looks on the outward appearance, but the Lord looks on the heart." But
the Lord said to Samuel, "Do not look on his appearance or on the height of
his stature, because I have rejected him. For the Lord sees not as man sees:
man looks on the outward appearance, but the Lord looks on the heart." But
the Lord said to Samuel, "Do not look on his appearance or on the height of
his stature, because I have rejected him. For the Lord sees not as man sees:
man look

Day 5

No Copy Work!

Recite 1 Samuel 16:7* for family & friends

Color or highlight the verse picture, then tear it out
and display it somewhere you'll see it often

Write out 1 Samuel 16:7 on a memory card
(or use the free printable cards at writetheword.com)
and add it to your memory stack

Review the cards in your memory pile

man looks on the outward appearance, but the Lord looks on the heart." But
the Lord said to Samuel, "Do not look on his appearance or on the height of
his stature, because I have rejected him. For the Lord sees not as man sees:
man looks on the outward appearance, but the Lord looks on the heart." But
the Lord said to Samuel, "Do not look on his appearance or on the height of
his stature, because I have rejected him. For the Lord sees not as man sees:
man looks on the outward appearance, but the Lord looks on the heart." But
the Lord said to Samuel, "Do not look on his appearance or on the height of
his stature, because I have rejected him. For the Lord sees not as man sees:
man looks on the outward appearance, but the Lord looks on the heart." But

For the Lord sees not as man sees man looks on the outward appearance but the Lord looks on the heart

1 Samuel 16:7

Proverbs 23:26

My son, give me your heart, and let your eyes observe my ways

Day 1: New week, new verse! Read the verse together 3x, then trace it, and copy below.

My son, give me your heart, and let your eyes observe my ways.
Proverbs 23:26

Day 2: Can you figure out which words are missing? Read the verse together 3x, then trace it and copy below.

_____ son, give _____ your heart, and let your eyes observe _____ ways. Proverbs 23:26

Day 3: More missing words! Can you recite the verse without help? Say the verse together 3x; then trace and copy below.

_____ son, give _____ your

heart, _____ _____ your eyes

observe _____ ways.

Proverbs 23:26

Day 4: Can you say the verse without help today? Fill in all the missing words, trace, and copy the verse below.

_____ son, give _____ _____

heart, _____ _____ _____ eyes

observe _____ ways.

Proverbs 23:26

My son, give me your heart, and let your eyes observe my ways. My son, give me your heart, and let your eyes observe my ways. My son, give me your heart, and let your eyes observe my ways. My son, give me your heart, and let your eyes observe[a] my ways. My son, give me your heart, and let your eyes observe my ways. My son, give me your heart, and let your eyes observe my ways. My son, give me your heart, and let your eyes observe my ways. My son, give me your heart, and let your eyes observe[a] my ways. My son, give me your heart, and let your eyes observe my ways. My son, give

Day 5

No Copy Work!

Recite Proverbs 23:26 for family & friends

Color or highlight the verse picture, then tear it out and display it somewhere you'll see it often

Write out Proverbs 23:26 on a memory card (or use the free printable cards at writetheword.com) and add it to your memory stack

Review the cards in your memory pile

heart, and let your eyes observe my ways. My son, give me your heart, and let your eyes observe my ways. My son, give me your heart, and let your eyes observe[a] my ways. My son, give me your heart, and let your eyes observe my ways. My son, give me your heart, and let your eyes observe my ways. My son, give me your heart, and let your eyes observe my ways. My son, give me your heart, and let your eyes observe[a] my ways. My son, give me your heart, and let your eyes observe my ways. My son, give me your heart, and let your eyes observe my ways. My son, give me your heart, and let your eyes observe my ways. My son, give me your heart, and let your eyes observe[a] my ways. My son, give me your heart, and let your eyes observe my ways. My son, give me your heart, and let your eyes observe my

My son

give me your

heart

and let your

eyes

observe

my ways

Yes, Dad?
I'm listening

Proverbs 23:26

Psalm 119:11

I have stored up your word in my heart, that I might not sin against you

Day 1: New week, new verse! Read the verse together 3x, then trace it, and copy below.

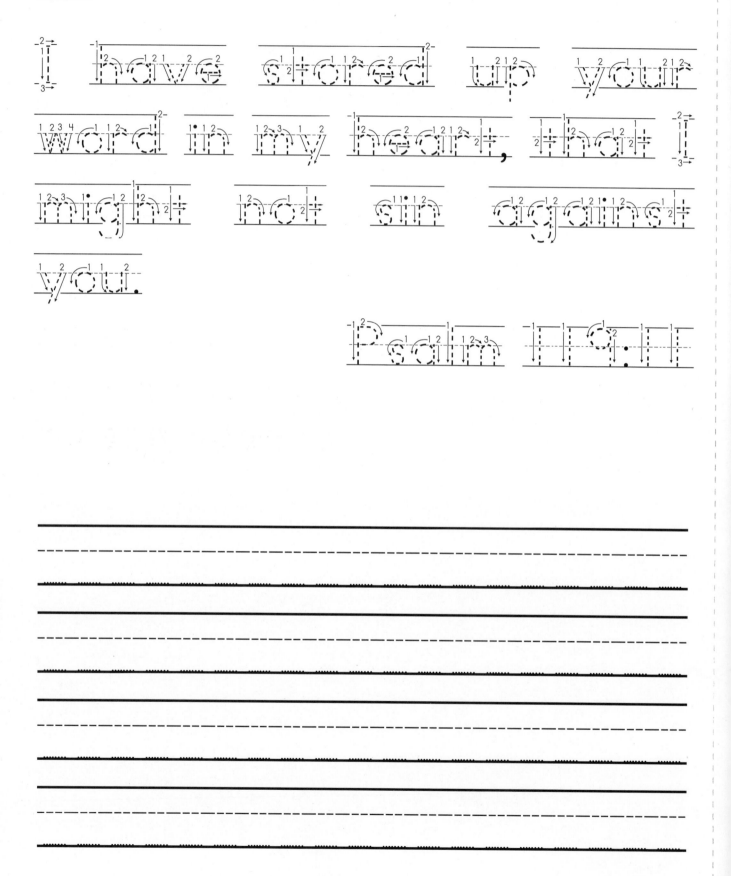

I have stored up your word in my heart, that I might not sin against you.

Psalm 119:11

Day 2: Can you figure out which words are missing? Read the verse together 3x, then trace it and copy below.

I have stored up _____ word in ___ heart, that I might not sin against _____.

Psalm 119:11

Day 3: More missing words! Can you recite the verse without help? Say the verse together 3x; then trace and copy below.

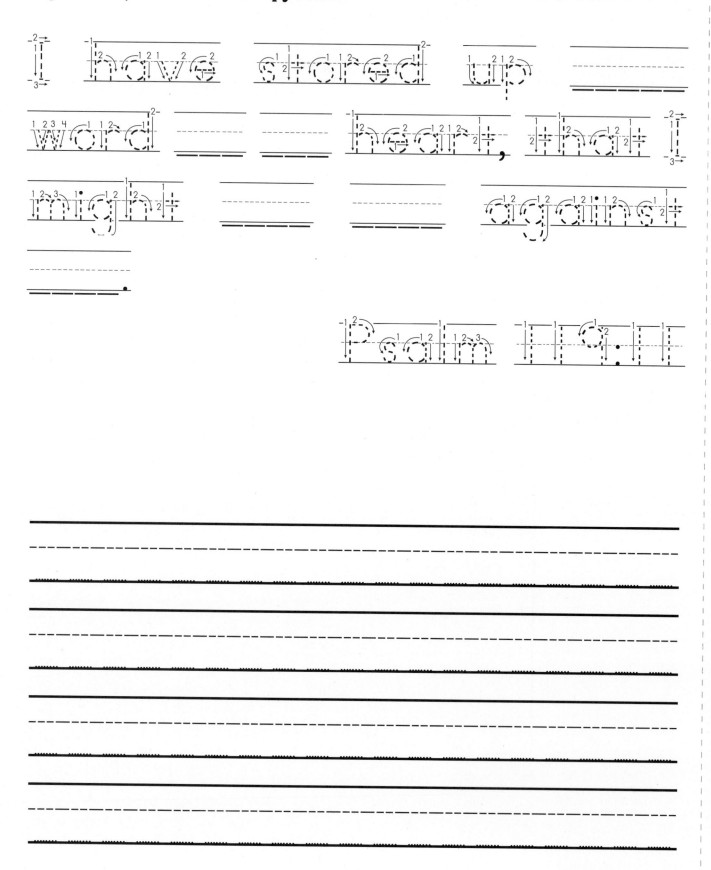

I have stored up _____ word _____ heart, that I might _____ _____ against _____.

Psalm 119:11

Day 4: Can you say the verse without help today? Fill in all the missing words, trace, and copy the verse below.

_____ have stored _____ _____

word _____ _____ heart, _____

_____ might _____ _____ against

_____

_____.

Psalm 119:11

that I might not sin against you. I have stored up your word in my heart, that I might not sin against you. I have stored up your word in my heart, that I might not sin against you. I have stored up your word in my heart, that I might not sin against you. I have stored up your word in my heart, that I might not sin against you. I have stored up your word in my heart, that I might not sin against you. that I might not sin against you. I have stored up your word in my heart, that I might not sin against you. I have stored up your word in my heart, that I might not sin against you. I have stored up your word in my heart, that I might not sin against you. I have stored up your word in my heart, that I might not sin against you. I have stored up your word in my heart, that I might not sin against you.

Day 5

No Copy Work!

Recite Psalm 119:11 for family & friends

Color or highlight the verse picture, then tear it out
and display it somewhere you'll see it often

Write out Psalm 119:11 on a memory card
(or use the free printable cards at writetheword.com)
and add it to your memory stack

Review the cards in your memory pile

heart, that I might not sin against you. I have stored up your word in my heart, that I might not sin against you. I have stored up your word in my heart, that I might not sin against you. I have stored up your word in my heart, that I might not sin against you. I have stored up your word in my heart, that I might not sin against you. I have stored up your word in my heart, that I might not sin against you. That I might not sin against you. I have stored up your word in my heart, that I might not sin against you. I have stored up your word in my heart, that I might not sin against you. I have stored up your word in my heart, that I might not sin against you. I have stored up your word in my heart, that I might not sin against you. I have stored up your word in my heart, that I

I have
STORED UP
your
Word
IN MY HEART
that I might not
sin
AGAINST YOU

Psalm 119:11

Congratulations!

*"But solid food is for the mature, who because of practice†
have their senses trained to discern good and evil."*
Hebrews 5:14 NASB

When I first began memorizing the word, I was overwhelmed. There were so many verses I wanted to learn, and I had no idea where to start. But the Lord strengthened me with a word from Hebrews 5:14: "solid food is for the mature, *who on account of habit*, have their senses trained to discern good and evil." It may seem like an obscure verse, but the Lord greatly encouraged me: if you want to learn the word, it's not going to happen overnight. But if you begin this habit of memorizing and training yourself in God's word, you will mature. Gradually, you will be able to handle more and more and more.

I hope this was your experience as you completed *Write the Word*. Maybe you (or your child) only knew a few verses initially, but as you learned and applied the verses in day-to-day conversations, did you see a change? Did the Lord remind you of his word in moments when you needed help? Did you have a reference point to encourage or correct your child and show him more of God's heart from the word? My prayer is that you did.

Regardless of whether you have "seen" results with your child(ren) this year, continue to sow the word into them. Continue to hold these verses before them. The Lord has promised his "word ...shall not return ...empty," but will "accomplish that which I purpose." (Isaiah 55:11) Whether your child responds today or not, the Holy Spirit has the materials to call, convict, and encourage in just the right moment. And you have the word in your heart, too, hidden away to share, at the Lord's leading.

If the Lord allows for future volumes of *Write the Word*, we hope to share more books, for Gospel Verses, the Psalms, Proverbs, or for a teenager facing new choices and temptations. If we have left out a favorite verse, just create your own card and add it to your weekly review stack; or try to work it in using another suggested memory method.

If you've followed along through the year, I hope this blessed your family. Since we are so new, your feedback is deeply appreciated and will be strongly considered if we do this again. Did you love it? Hate it? Wish it had something more? Wish you could make a few changes or that we'd include your favorite verse next time?

Stop by on social media; or email me directly at katherine@writetheword.com. We'd love to hear from you or see pictures of your family using *Write the Word*.

Interested in future updates? Follow along on Facebook, find us on Instagram @writetheword_com, or visit our website, writetheword.com. Thank you for sharing this journey with us!

To God be the glory,

Katherine

---

† *Alternate translations: "on account of habit" (Darby) "by constant use" (NIV)*

"...from childhood you have known the sacred writings which are able to give you the wisdom that leads to salvation through faith which is in Christ Jesus."

2 Timothy 3:15 NASB

Memory Helps for *Write the Word* and Beyond

If you'd like to keep scripture memory as a part of your home, here are a few more ideas to keep the word fresh and fun. Many of these also work well in a classroom or Sunday school setting.

- ## Memorize with Music

  This is one of the most fun and natural ways to help our children memorize. Albums like Steve Green's *Hide 'Em in Your Heart,* or the anything from the *Seeds' Family* Collection is excellent; and will have your kids effortlessly memorizing while they're bouncing around the room cleaning up. Matt Papa and Ross King's *Every Last Word* album skillfully shares word-for-word chapters, and really captures the spirit of the passages. A simple search across YouTube or Instagram will reveal dozens of artists who have created their own songs. If you're musically inclined, you may want to try your hand at writing one, too.

- ## Memorize with Movement

  Write each word of a verse on an index card or piece of paper. Scatter the cards around the room. Ask the kids to jump from word to word in the correct order of the verse. This could also be done outside with chalk.

- ## Memorize by Removing Words

  Write each word from the verse on an index card. Recite the verse out loud together. Remove several words and recite it aloud together again. Keep removing words until the whole verse can be recited without any cards.

- ## Memorize by Recording (your own voice)

  Read the verse or portion of verses into a voice recording app or video. Then replay and listen, over and over and over. This method is especially helpful for longer portions of scripture. If you don't want to record, you can also try listening to an audio Bible on repeat.

- ## Incorporate Memory into your Dinner (or breakfast or lunch) Routine

  Attach 10 popsicle sticks together with tape, accordion style. After the sticks are taped together, write a few words from the verse on each stick with a permanent marker. Place the popsicle-stick accordions into a jar on your kitchen table. Take the jar out at mealtime and quiz each other. If someone gets stuck, read a few of the words listed on the first popsicle stick to help. (This could be simplified to be written on paper or index cards and left on the table. Something about the popsicle sticks seemed to make it more fun for our children.)

- ## Memorize with (your own) Art

  If you're artistically inclined, keep a scripture art journal where you write out verses using different fonts and pictures.

Ready to get serious about Bible Memory?
Find even more ideas on our website, www.writetheword.com

*"All scripture is inspired by God and profitable
for teaching, for reproof, for correction, for training in righteousness;
so that the man of God may be adequate,
equipped for every good work."*

2 Timothy 3:16-17 NASB